D0064948

NUMBER 71

THE ENGLISH
EXPERIENCE

ITS RECORD IN EARLY PRINTED BOOKS
PUBLISHED IN FACSIMILE

LEONARD DIGGES

STRATIOTICOS

LONDON 1579

DA CAPO PRESS
THEATRVM ORBIS TERRARVM LTD.
AMSTERDAM 1968 NEW YORK

The publishers acknowledge their gratitude
to the Syndics of Cambridge University Library
for their permission to reproduce
the Library's copy.

Published in 1968 by
Theatrum Orbis Terrarum Ltd.,
O.Z. Voorburgwal 85, Amsterdam
&
Da Capo Press
- a division of Plenum Publishing Corporation -
227 West 17th Street, New York. 10011
Library of Congress Catalog Card Number:

68 - 54641
Printed in The Netherlands

¶ An Arithmeticall Militare Treatiſe, named
STRATIOTICOS:
Compendiouſly teaching the Science of Nūbers,
as vvell in Fractions as Integers, and ſo much of the Rules and Æquations Algebraicall and Arte of Numbers
Coſsicall, as are requiſite for the Profeſsion of a Soldiour.

Together with the Moderne Militare Diſcipline, Offices, Lawes and
Dueties in euery wel gouerned Campe and Armie to be obſerued :
Long ſince attēpted by LEONARD DIGGES Gentleman,
Augmented, digeſted, and lately finiſhed, by
THOMAS DIGGES, his Sonne.

Whereto he hath alſo adioyned certaine Queſtions *of great Ordinaunce,*
reſolued in his other Treatize of Pyrotechny *and great*
Artillerie, hereafter to bee publiſhed.

VIVET POST FVNERA VIRTVS.

AT LONDON:
Printed by Henrie Bynneman.
Anno Domini. 1579.

DROIT · ET·LOYAL

¶ To the Right Honourable my fin
gular good Lord, the Lorde Robert Dudley,
Earle of *Leicester*, *Baron* of Denbigh, Knighte of the
moſt noble order of the Garter, and one of hir
Maieſties moſt Honourable priuate
Counſayle.

Ighte Honourable,
finding my ſelfe to youre
Lordſhip deepely bounde,
as well for my preferment
to hir *Maieſties* ſeruice, as
for ſundrie other fauoures
continuallye powred on
me, I haue carefullye be-
thought my ſelfe, whyche
way I mighte render ſome
teſtimonye of a gratefull
minde. And hauing ſpent
many of my yeares in reducing the Sciences *Mathematicall,*
from *Demonſtratiue Contemplatione,* to *Experimentall Actions,*
for the ſeruice of my *Prince* and *Countrey :* (beeyng thereto
greately ayded by the *Practiſes, Obſeruations, Monuments,* and
Conferences of my Father, with the rareſt Souldyoures of hys
time) haue among ſundrie other diſcourſes of *Nauigation,* of
Fortification, of *Pyrotechnie,* and great *Artillerie,* long ſithence
comenced, latelie finiſhed this *Arithmeticall* Treatiſe, wholy
applyed to *Militare* affayres. And finding not onely by the
whole courſe of *Hiſtories* of all times and Countreys, howe
Kingdomes haue flouriſhed in all felicitie, whereas this Arte
hath bene embraced, and duelie practiſed, and cótrarywiſe,
how moſt happie *Empires* after warlike *Diſcipline* haue bin
corrupted, haue fallen to ruine, and miſerable ſeruitude : but
alſo by experience euen in theſe dayes ſeene, what extreame diſorders growe in thoſe Armyes, where *Militare*

A.iij.   I   et

The Epistle Dedicatorie.

Lawes, and *Ordinances,* haue bene neglected : haue thought this matter not vnfit to be remembred in thefe our flourifhing and quiet times, that as the *Pallace* of this moft happie *Kingdome,* (ruled by a Soucrayne *Princeffe,* whofe wifedome and rare vertues all *Europe* haue in admiration) is inwardlye moft curiouflie garnifhed with the perfection of *Sciences* Humane and Diuine, with fundry *Artes,* with Riches, Reft, Wealth, and Pleafure comparable with, or furpaffing anye other of Chriftendome : fo wifhing alfo it maye not wante (when need fhall be) the *Roofe,* and outward couering, to defend and garde it from the winde and Rayne, and furious ftormes of Forraigne *Tempeftes.* And as the Fame of an honourable enterprife, vnder your Lordfhips conduite generally expected, did firft moue me to employ my *Mathematicall Mufes,* vpon this *Militare Argument,* fo fithence hauing in fome poynts altered, and augmented the firft *Originall,* to your Lordfhip then prefented, and now fully digefted and finifhed the fame, (wel knowing the *Methode* fuche, as hytherto in no Language hath bin publifhed, and your *Lordfhip* for Wifedome, Learning, and *Experience,* (hauing long fithence borne honourable Office in the Field) fullie able of your felfe to difcerne the *Veritie* and *Valour* of this Worke.) In difcharge of fome part of my dutie, I prefume to prefent, and publifh the fame vnder the *Protection* of your Name. As a *Patrone,* I aduow my felfe to honor, by all other due dutifull meanes I can. And crauing fauourable acceptation of this my homelie dutifull prefent, humbly leaue your Lordfhip to the direction of the *Almightie,* who graunt you a long profperous life, garnifhed with cotinuall encreafe of honourable actions, to the amplyfying of his Glorie and true *Religion,* the faithfull feruice of hir moft excellent *Maieftie,* and comfort of vs all that loue and honour you.

Your Honours dutifully at commaynd,

THOMAS DIGGES.

THE PREFACE
to the Reader.

Auing ſpent my youngeſt yeres euen from my Cradle in the Sciences Liberal, & eſpecially in ſearching the moſt difficult & curious Demonſtrations Mathematicall, by proofe at laſt I found the ſaying of that wiſe Tarentine & eloquent Romane moſt true: That if it wer poſsible for a mortall man by power Diuine to bée transferred into ſome ſolitarie Garden of incomparable pleaſure, and there all things that could be wiſhed as it were by the hands of Angels to be miniſtred vnto him, enioying perfect Health, Strength, and all other good giftes of Nature, that were requiſite to a ful perfection of delite both in minde and body, ſaue onely that it ſhould not be lawfull for him to haue Societie or cóference with any man to communicate the ſtate of his Felicitie: That notwithſtanding all theſe delites, his life ſhould ſéeme tedious, and all thoſe pleaſures loathſome.

Euen ſo, albeit the ſtraunge varietie of Inuentions in the more ſubtile part of theſe Mathematical Demonſtrations did bréede in me for a time a ſingular delectation, yet finding none, or very few, with whome to conferre & communicate thoſe my delites, (& remembring alſo that graue ſentence of Diuine Plato, that we are not borne for our ſelues, but alſo for our Parents, Countrie, and A.iij.   Friends)

Friends.) After I grew to yeares of riper iudgement, I haue wholy bent my self to reduce those Imaginatiue Cōtemplations, to sensible Practicall Conclusions : as well thereby to haue some companions of those my delectable studies, as also to be able, when time is, to employ thē to the seruice of my Prince and Countrie.

First therefore, by Demonstrations Mathematical finding the great imperfections in the Arte of Nauigation, & grosse Errours practised by the masters and Mariners of this our age, I sought by reason to perswade with some of them to alter & reforme their Charts, Instruments, and erronious Rules, shewing them infallible Demonstrations of their Errours.

In lyke sort, perusing the Auntient Romane Discipline for the Warres, their exquisite order of Trayning the Soldiorie euen from their infancie, in sundry sorts of hardenesse, Labour and Actiuitie : Their inuincible order in Marching, Fighting, and Encamping, together with their diuine Lawes to kéepe their Armies in obedience. Finding also by conferring the Romane Histories, how afterwards by the dissolute disorder of Emperours this Discipline was corrupted, ŷ Romane People disarmed, a Pretorian Garde maintained, which licenciously liuing, murdered & deposed the Emperours thēselues, & solde the Empire for money to whom they list: And so by little and little ŷ Maiestie of that Monarchie defaced, & the Romane People which before gaue Lawes to ŷ world afterward most seruilely to abide, not onely all kinde of iniurie and villanie among themselues, but also inuaded, spoyled, sacked and conquered by the Hunes, Vandalles, Gothes, and other barbarous Nations.

The whole course of these Histories conferred with the rising and falling also of the Asirian, Persian and Macedonian Monarchies, did plainely demonstrate vnto mée, that the well and euill vsing of this Millitarie Discipline

pline among all naturall causes was the greatest, oz ra=
ther the onely occasion, of the aduauncing, establishing,
oz razing and defacing of all Monarchies, Empires, Kingdomes, & Common Weales. And haue therefoze with sun=
dzy Captaines conferred, and earnestly perswaded, that
as in all other Artes and Sciences we ayde our selues vs
Precedents from Antiquitie, so in this Arte of Discipline
Millitare, so cozrupted, oz rather vtterly extinguished, we
should repaire to those Fountaines of perfection, and accõ=
modate them to the seruice of our Time.

But as among many with whome I haue conferred,
aswell of mine owne Countrimen, as Straungers, albeit
I found some one oz other of the better learned and best
experienced, that ioyned with me in opinion, yet general=
ly (such is the imperfection of mans nature) if they had
bene in a few skirmishes, oz taken any degrée in Fielde,
they thought it so great a disgrace, that any thing should
be desired in a Souldiour that wanted in themselues, that
pzesentlie they woulde giue their Definitiue Sentence,
that the Time was chaunged, the Warres were altered,
and the furie of Ordinaunce suche, as all those Romane
Ozders were méere toyes once to be talked of in these
oure dayes : As though the Heauens and Elementes had
chaunged their Natures, oz Men and Weapons so al=
tered, as no humaine reason might attaine to consider the
difference. Oz as though the Romane Orders foz ỹ Field
(a very few excepted) were not moze cõuenient, moze ser=
uiceable, and moze Inuincible, (all alterations conside=
red) euen in these our dayes, than they were foz that age
wherein they were vsed and pzactized.

In like sozt by Masters, Pilotes, and Mariners, I haue
bene aunswered, that my Demonstrations were pzetie de=
uises : but if I had bene in any Sea seruices, I should
finde all these my Inuentions méere toyes, & their Rules
onely pzactizeable : Adding farder, that whatsoeuer I
could

could in Paper by Demonstrations perswade, by Experience on Seas they found their Charts and Instruments true and infallible.

These constant asseuerations from men of that Profession, euen in their owne Arte, did make me halfe distrust my Demonstrations, and to thinke that Reason had abused me, or that there were some such Misterie in Sea seruice, as no Land mans reason might attaine vnto.

To resolue my selfe of this Paradoxe, I spent a xb. weékes in continual Sea seruices vpon the Ocean, where by proofe I found, and those verie Masters themselues could not but confesse, that Experience did no lesse plainely discouer the Errours of their Rules, than my Demonstrations. Sithens which time, I haue learned no more to be abused with the Opinions of men, what Office, or Degrée soeuer they haue born, or what Fame soeuer go of them, if Reason be repugnant to their Opinions. For

Magni sæpè Viri, mendacia magna loquuntur :
Ratio dux fida Sophorum.

And Reason techeth me, how barbarous that common opinion is, that an English man will be trained in a few Weékes to be a perfect Souldiour. For if a Mason, a Painter, or other Mechanicall Artificer be scarcely able in seuen yeares to learne the perfection of his Science, shal we thinke the Art of a Souldiour so base and abiect, that it is to be attained in a few Weékes or Monethes? But such is the Vanitie of the common sort, that if they haue caried Armes, and bene in a few seruices, they presently thinke themselues worthy the name of perfect Soldiours.

Yet Guillaume du Bellay, Seigneur de Langeay, a famous General of our age, hauing set down a great number of parts requisite in a trained Soldiour, and also in a trained Band, concludeth with this resolution: That such a Souldiour or Band, as is able Encamping, Marching,

and

and Fighting, to execute all those his prescribed orders, albeit he neuer saw the Enimie in the face, yet I holde hym (sayth that Generall) an olde Souldyoure, or a trayned Bande. And otherwise, if he haue bin neuer so long in the Warres, yea if it were possible for him to be in a thousand Seruices, if he be not able to perfourme those Orders, I account of him but as of a raw vntrayned Souldioure.

But seing it woulde require at the least an whole age, and the direction of some rare Prince to reduce Souldiorie to the antique perfection, and therefore in vayne for anye priuate man to intermedle therewithall: yet somewhat to discouer that grosse Errour, that Souldiarie maye so soone be learned, and that we may haue some tast and feeling at least of oure owne ignoraunce and imperfection, and to awake our Nation out of that secure Dreame, hauing partlie by experience my selfe seene, what extreame disorders growe, and dishonors are recepued for wante of Militare Discipline: I haue therefore thought good, according to the best obseruations of oure Moderne Warres, and Seruice of this Time, to sette downe the Office and dutie of eache person and calling, passing from a Priuate Souldiour, to a Generall, with certayne Militare Lawes to be obserued in euery well gouerned Armie.

And albeit I well knowe, these matters Militare, (not being Mathematicall, and therefore not to be confirmed by inuincible Demonstration, but as Philosophie, Lawe, Physicke, and suche other Artes, standing on probabilitie onelie) may and will in many opinions be impugned, yet hauing discourse of Reason, with Authoritie, and Example, not only from Antiquitie, but also of the most notable and famous Souldyours of our Age in Christendome, as well in their priuate as publike Actions, to confirme and ratifie these orders and Discipline by me deliuered, I am in the better hope, the wise, and best experienced, will not mislike my Trauels, tending chiefelie to this ende, that

a.   our

To the Reader.

our Nation in thys happye peace maye not reſt altogyther careleſſe of Warres, but in ſuche ſorte prepare theyr Myndes and Bodyes, that when néede ſhall be, they may be found the more readie, and capable of orders Millitare, which do ſo well conforme with Ciuill and peaceable gouernement, as nothing more.

Howbeit, the corruption of Millitare Diſcipline, and licentious liuing of the Souldyoure of oure tyme, hathe made them odyous, who of all other ſhoulde moſt be embraced and loued, if theſe Erroures were reſourmed, and this their Arte dulie practiſed.

For who ought to be a greater louer of Peace than he? who chiefelie in Warres is to endure Payne, Perill, Hunger, Cold, and infinite other diſeaſes.

Who ought to be more faythfull to hys Prince, and Countrey, than he? whoſe Oth and profeſſion is to Sacrifice himſelfe for the ſame.

In whome ought there to be a greater loue and feare of God than in him: that euerie day committing himſelfe to a thouſande dangers and hazardes of life, hathe moſt néede of his ayde and helpe.

Theſe things conſidered of the Founders of the moſt honourable Kingdomes and Monarchyes of the Worlde, did cauſe them by all meanes to embrace this Arte, and togither with Artes Ciuill, to trayne theyr Subiectes in this Science Militare, as héereafter more particularly I ſhall haue cauſe to declare, hauing in this diſcourſe no farther relyed vpon the Diſcipline of the Antiquitie, than by Reaſon, Example, and Authoritie of the moſt famous Generals and Souldyoures of thys Age in Chriſtendome, I haue founde neceſſarie to diſſent from ſuche brute cuſtomes as the Barbarous Gothes, &c. lefte vs, and oure delicious ydle ignoraunce hathe ſtill nouriſhed among vs, embracing all ſuch Moderne Ordinances and vſances, as are not quite repugnante to all good Diſcipline,

and

To the Reader.

and by no meanes to bée allowed oz tollerated.

The whole Treatise I haue deuided into thzée Bokes.

The firste Boke compendiouslie declareth the fiue vulgare Arithmeticall kyndes, with the extraction of the Rootes Quadrate, and Cubicall, in whole numbers, and also in Fractions. Thys was begon, and almost finished by my Father.

In the second Boke I haue taught the same kinds in numbers Cossicall, with so muche of the Arte of Algebra, as I fynde necessarie foz a Souldioure, and thereto adioyned sundzie Questions in diuers of the pzincipall Offices of the Field.

And bycause suche Noblemen oz Gentlemen as wyll applye themselues to that honourable pzofession, maye know how in manye other Seruices Militare Arithmetike maye stande them in stéede, I haue added the thirde Boke of Militare Lawes, Offices, and Duties.

Last of all I haue set downe certayne Questions touching greate Ordinance, to be considered, and resolued of suche as haue the perfection of the Arte of manedging Great Artillerie, giuing also vnto suche as are oz will be pzactizers therein, some light, howe to dizecte the ozder of their Practises. And if they be founde of that difficultie that none will vndertake to meddle with theyz resolution (as I sée these my Laboures gratefully accepted) I wyll imparte wyth my Countreymen my Treatise of Greate Artillerie and Pyrotechnie, delyuering the same wyth sundzye rare seruiceable secretes, hytherto not put in execution by anye Chzistian Prince.

Otherwise, by the example of my Father, Pythagorical lyc I wyll contente my selfe Per manus tradere, and to communicate them onely wyth a fewe selecte friendes.

a.ij. And

To the Reader.

And so good Reader I committe thée to the Treatise it selfe, wherein if thou finde any thing that dothe contente thée, yéelde due thankes to the Patrone of the Worke, whose honourable disposition in fauouring and aduauncing all Vertue, and chiefelie the studious of these Liberall Sciences, with many especiall fauoures vppon my selfe, hath prouoked, or rather inforced me, to take in hande this presente Worke, finished the 13. of October.

1572.

VNI DEO, PATRIAE, PATRIAEQVE PATRONAE.

THOMAS DIGGES.

The Contentes of this Treatise briefly ensue.

The first Booke Arithmeticall.

The seconde Booke Algebraicall.

The third Militare, conteyning Offices,
Lawes, Stratagemes. &c.

The Bookes alreadie publifhed
by the Authoure of thys
Treatise.

A Generall *Pronostication* long sithence publifhed by his Father, after perufed by hymfelfe, and thereto adioyned the frame of the Worlde, according to *Copernicus Hipothefis*, vpon the mobilitie of the Earth.

A *Geometricall* Treatife called *Pantometria*, begon by hys Father, augmented and finifhed by himfelfe.

A Booke in Latine entituled *Ala, feu Scala Mathematica*, deliue-

deliuering fundrye Demonſtrations, for the finding of the *Paralaxis* of any Comet, or other Celeſtiall bodie, wyth the correction of the Erroures in the vſe of *Radius Aſtronomicus.*

This preſent Arithmeticall *STRATIOTICOS,* deuided into three Bookes.

Bookes begon by the Author, heereafter to be publiſhed.

1 A *Treatiſe* of the Arte of *Nauigation*, bewraying the groſſe *Erroures* by oure Mayſters, and Marriners practiſed, deliuering new Rules, and *Inſtruments* infallible, and practiceable, ſome alſo accommodate to the vulgare Capacitie, with a diſcourſe *Demonſtratiue*, vpon ſundry *Hypotheſeis* of the *Nauticall Compaſſe* hys *Variation*, diſcouering Rules for the inuention of the *Longitude* at all tymes to bee practiſed, as certayne as by the ☉ *Eclipſes.*

2 A briefe Treatiſe of *Architecture Nauticall*, wherin is deliuered *Rules* infallible vpon anye one forme or Modell of *Excellencie* founde, to buylde Shyppes for all burthens of lyke perfection and propertie to the *Patterne*, wyth certayne kyndes of forcible fyghtes, Lawes alſo and Orders in Sea ſeruices to be obſerued.

3 *Commentaries* vpon the *Reuolutions* of *Copernicus*, by euidente Demonſtrations grounded vpon late *Obſeruations*, to ratifye and confirme hys *Theorikes* and *Hypotheſis*, wherein alſo Demonſtratiuelie ſhall be diſcuſſed, whether it bee poſsible vpon the vulgare *Theſis* of the Earthes *Stabilitie*, to delyuer any true *Theorike* voyde of ſuch irregular Motions, and other abſurdities, as repugne the whole *Principles* of *Philoſophie* naturall, and apparant groundes of common *Reaſon.*

4 *A Booke* of Dialling, teaching the Arte to garniſh all the *Regular* and transformed bodyes, in his *Pantometria* menti-

mentioned, with houres vulgare and *Planetare*, *Signes*, *Azi-muthes*, *Almicanters*, &c. and also to make all sortes of Dials, *Anulare*, *Cylinders*, *Nauicles*, *Hydriacles*. &c.

5 *A Treatise* of Great *Artillerie*, and *Pyrotechnye*, contey-ning sundrie Demonstrations *Geometricall*, and *Instruments* exactly to shoote in all sorts of Peeces at all degrees of *Ran-dons*, both by day and night, with other new Inuentions, and seruiceable secretes, begon by his Father after long *Experi-ence*, augmented, and heereafter to be finished by himselfe.

6 *A Treatise* of *Fortification* of *Townes*, *Fortes*, and *Campes*, by a *Methode* cleane repugnant to anye hitherto practised, conteyning sundrie sorts of more forcible formes, with *Rules* of great facilitie by certayne *Instruments Geometricall* to stake them out, and readilie to set downe in good order an whole Armie, with all his *Regiments*, *Footemen*, *Horsemen*, *Munition*, *Carriadges*, &c. in most commodious and strong maner that place will permitte.

All *these and other long sithens, the Author had finished and published, had not the* Infernall Furies, *enuying such his* Foelici-tie, *and happie* Societie *with his* Mathematicall Muses, *for many yeares so tormented him with* Lawe-Brabies, *that he hath bene enfor-ced to discontinue those his de-lectable* Studies,

To implore in Ayde from Iupiters *Pallace,*

PHILORTHVS PHILARETES and

PHILOMATHES

Againste

APLESTODOLEROS AMOVSEOS

MISOGENAIOS.

DABIT DEVS HIS QVOQVE FINEM.

¶ The kindes of *Algorisme*, whiche I
intend briefely to treate of, as vvell in broken as whole, are these, *Numeration, Addition,
Subtraction, Multiplication, Partition,
Reduction, Progression,* with the finding of the *Rootes, Square,*
and *Cubicall.*

The first Booke.

Of Numeration. Chap. 1.

Number is the multitude of Unites sette
togither, as 2. 3. 4. &c. All Numbers may
bée exp2essed by these Characters following.

1 2 3 4 5 6 7 8 9 0

Whose simple value by themselues considered, you maye héere-vnder beholde.

j tj itj itij v vj vtj vitj ix 0

The Ciphra 0 augmenteth places, but of himselfe signi-
fieth not. To number anye summe nothing else it is, but to
declare the value of euerie Figure placed. So many places
are in your wo2ke, as there be Elementes from the righte
hand to the left. Euery Figure in the first place betokeneth
himselfe, and so towarde the left side, tenne times so muche
as he was the place befo2e.

Example.

The value of the figures placed.

M M
M M M M M
C X M C X M C X one
The last 1 1 1 1 1 1 1 1 1 *The first place*
B.

To

To auoyde confusion, and to atteyne quicke and readie numbring. In greate numbers handle your summe thus. The fourth place whiche repzesenteth a M. let him haue a pzicke ouer his head, the fifte and sixt omitted the seauenth marke, the eight & ninth ouerpasse, the tēth note. Likewise the eleuenth and twelfth not regarded, point the thirtéenth, & so forthe two places neglected titling the nexte. Example.

$$2\overset{.}{1}09\overset{.}{7}46\overset{.}{2}5\overset{.}{3}2\overset{.}{4}13$$

Go to the last place noted oz pzicked, whiche is on the left hand, reckning all the Characters afoze that point leftward, with the figure vnder him, togither, euē as their places from that title do appoynt, passing fozth not staying to all the poynts, giuing to that, and to euerie of them thys tearme Thousand, returning again to the next figure significatiue ensuing the pzicke. Now toward the right side still renning youre course againe by the points, not forgetting this terme Thousand so oft to be named as you haue points to come vntill euerie figure is valued. Behold the counting of the summe immediately befoze wzitten. 21 M M M M. Bycause ther be four pzickes, I giue this tearme thousand four times, repzesented by this letter M. Nowe returne agayne to ŷ next figure of signification, following the pzicke saying 97 M M M. 462. M M. 532 M. 413: Thus doe of all such like. Héere néede no moe wozds for so playne a matter.

There be thzée sozts of numbers, the one a Digit, ŷ other an Article, the last a mixt oz a cōpound. Al nūbers not excéeding 9 vnites, are called Digits, as 1 2 3 4 5 6 7 8 9. Articles be nūbers of tennes, oz those ŷ may be deuided into 10 equal parts, as 10,20,30,40,340. &c. The cōpound is a nubmer of both, as 12,13,14,24. &c. Of Numeratiō this héere sufficeth.

Of Addition. Chap. 2.

TO adde is to gather and knit in one many numbers oz Vnites, whereby the whole summe manifestly may appeare, as 3, 15 and 22 maketh 40 the whole &c.

Be

Beginne your collection from the right hand to the lefte, from the lowest number to the highest of that row, & what Digit resulteth, subscribe. Set your numbers in due place, yea directly the one vnder the other, with a line drawen beneath them, as in the Example. And note so many articles as surmounteth in any order ought to be adioyned to ẏ next rowme or row leftward, calling thē by the name of Vnitées, coueying the Digittes or Ciphre euer vnder the line. Now gather these summes in one which follow 9554. 4030. 9923. Place them rightely the firste vnder the first, and so correspondently, as by example héere appeareth.

$$\begin{array}{cccc} 9 & 5 & 5 & 4 \\ 4 & 0 & 3 & 0 \\ 9 & 9 & 2 & 3 \\ \hline 2 & 3 & 5 & 0 & 7 \end{array}$$

Now adde 3 and 4 whiche make 7, omitting the 0 signifying nothing: write 7 vnder the line in place due, then 2, 3, and 5 is 10, put the Ciphre 0 vnder, kéeping the article in mind. Now 9, 0, 5, and one in memorie, yéeldeth 15. Put the Digit 5 beneath the line, not forgetting the article at the next order, 9, 4, 9, maketh 22, and 1 in mind 23, put 3 downe, and the two articles reposed in memorie a place farther. Behold vnder the line your total summe, with your figures right placed. The whole Addition is 2 3 5 0 7. How money of diuers kinds is added, you shall perceiue when you come to the Addition of Numbers Cossicall.

Of Subduction. Chap. 3.

TO subduce or subtray any sume, is wittily to pull a lesse fró a bigger núber, or an equall fró a like or equall, so ẏ ẏ remaine if it be any thing, do appeare. As if I take 35 fró 40, ther is left 5. In this kind you shal worke as afore from the righte side to the lefte, deducting the lower from the higher summe in that order subscribing the remnant. Also euery Element must haue his conuenient place, as is sayde of Addition, the one direct vnder the other. Note whésoeuer the vpper is the leſſe number, or a Ciphre, then ſhall you conſider the diſtance of the lower number from this article 10, and adioyne the ſame diſtance vnto the ſaide leſſer number, ſubſcribing it, giuing alwayes one vnite to the nexte Element.

Example.

From 1 3 0 4 0 5 3 I would haue 4 0 0 2 7 1 ſubducted, put them in right order, as enſueth.

```
    1  3  0  4  0  5  3
    4  0  0  2  7 .1
    ─────────────────────
       9  0  3  7  8  2
```

One from 3 remayneth 2 vnder the line with him in place mæte, 7 from 5 it may not, the diſtance of 7 from 10 is 3, wherefore I doe accompanie 3 with 5 and it maketh 8, put that 8 vnder, nowe 2 and 1 in memorie repoſed, noteth 3, from the Ciphre 0 it may not be, the diſtance of hym from 10 is 7, whiche put to the Ciphre maketh but 7. Let hym haue his place in like manner vnder. This Ciphre 0 enſuing, and 1 in minde, encreaſeth but 1. Take that from 4, remayneth 3, to be ſette vnder the line. Againe, the Ciphre 0 from this circle 0 ſubtracted nothing is lefte. This 0 muſt haue place vnder. Then 4 from 3 it may not. The diſtance of 4 from 10 is 6, whiche ioyned with 3, maketh 9 to be placed beneath the line, now one in memorie taken from 1, remayneth 0, wherefore this Cipre 0 ſhoulde be put vnder, vnleſſe it chance as it dothe hære in the laſt place. The ſumme remayning of this Subtraction, is 9 0 3 7 8 2, as appeareth vnder the line in the Example.

Of Multiplication.   Chap. 4

TO multiplie, is to find of two Numbers a nūber product the one in the other augmented, the which ſo often may conteyne the number multiplied, as there be of Unites in the Multiplicator. The leſſe is named the Multiplicator or
Multi-

Multiplyer, the other summe, oz number to be multiplyed.
In this kinde, you shall labour from the right side ꝛc. The
Elements there disposed in iust ozder, and wought as the
Examples following declare. I would multiplie 3 0 2 0 by
3, dispose your numbers thus.

The number to bee multiplyed.	}	3020
The digite that dothe multiplie.		3
The Producte.		9060

Nowe say 3 times 0 encreaseth nothing, conuey thys 0
vnder the line, 3 times 2 causeth 6, subscribe 6, thrice 0 ma=
keth nothing, write the Ciphze beneath the line. Thrice 3
pzoduceth 9, put him vnder. Beholde your summe beneath
the line 9 0 6 0. Bycause the multiplication of Digittes is
first necessarie to be knowen befoze any other Example be
written, I haue pzepared foz their augmentation a Table,
not a little conducing to Partition, as to the pzactiser after
shall appeare, the vse is this, you shall seeke the Digitte to
be multiplyed in the one side of the Table most commodi=
ous, the Multiplyer in the other, at the common meeting
of both, the Pzoduct sheweth himselfe.

Pythagoras Table.

1	2	3	4	5	6	7	8	9	10
2	4	6	8	10	12	14	16	18	20
3	6	9	12	15	18	21	24	27	30
4	8	12	16	20	24	28	32	36	40
5	10	15	20	25	30	35	40	45	50
6	12	18	24	30	36	42	48	54	60
7	14	21	28	35	42	49	56	63	70
8	16	24	32	40	48	56	64	72	80
9	18	27	36	45	54	63	72	81	90
10	20	30	40	50	60	70	80	90	100

This Table of the Pythagorians was taught vnto chil=

dzen, togither with their firſt letters, being in déede as neceſſarie to be conned by rote, and had in perfecte memozie foz the perfection of Arithmetike, as the common letters, oz ſpelling of Sillables are to the Grammarian. This Table therefoze firſt pzinte liuely in thy remembzance, and then boldly pzocéde farther, all difficultie I aſſure thée is paſt.

An other Example. I would multiplie 7 3 4 by 92.

The number multiplyed.	7 3 4
The *Multiplyer.*	9 2
	1468
	6606
The Producte.	67528

Your Figures on this wiſe placed, and a line vnder them dzawé, with ỹ firſt figure of your Multiplicator which is 2, beginne thus, ſaying two times 4 encreaſeth 8, put him vnder the line, euen with 4, the firſt of your number to be multiplyed. Then twice 3 maketh 6, conuey him vnder the line iuſt with 3, which is the ſeconde Character of your number to be multiplyed. Two tymes 7 is 14, place the Digitte 4 vnder 7 the thirde of your multiplyed number, and the article 1 a rowme farther, now daſhe 2 with your penne, his office perfozmed, being the firſt figure of your Multiplicator. Then to the other Character, the ſecond which is 9, ſaying, nine times 4 is 36, put the Digitte 6 vnder 9 youre ſeconde multiplicatoz, the articles kept in mind, then nine times 3 is 27, and 3 repoſed, yéeldeth 30. put this o vnder 4, and 3 in memozie foz the next place: nine times 7 is 63 and 3 in mind cauſeth 66, ſet 6 vnder 1, and the ſixe articles a place farther leftward, ſo by Addition you haue (as it is aboue vnder line wzitten) this ſumme 67528, the whole Multiplication.

Compendious formes of Multiplication.

IF you will multiplie by this article 10 100 1000 10000 &c. to ỹ núber which muſt be multiplied by theſe articles,

ad33

adde so many Ciphers as goeth before the Unite.

Example 36 by 10, put the Ciphre 0, and it is 360. Multiplie 45 by 100, adding the two Ciphres, is made 4500, and so of the rest. If by chance one Ciphre or many come in the beginning of the number that multiplieth, or the number to be multiplyed or both, put away all these Ciphres, reseruing them to the ende, multiplying the rest of the figures, and then adde al the Ciphres to the beginning or first place of the Product of that Multiplication. As 32000, by 2000, augmente 32 by 2, and put unto the Product, whiche is 64, those sire Ciphres, so is it 64000000. And when Ciphres by chance come within the numbers, you may ouerleape those of the Multiplicator. Also if you list to multiplie by 5, you may mediate or deuide your summe by 2 adding to the Product this Ciphre 0, which must occupie ye first place. Being odde, let 5 take the first roome, after the Mediation, not regarding the Unite left of the number to be diuided.

A rule vvhereby also the demonstration
of Multiplication may be gathered.

When you haue numbers to be multiplyed, diuide which summe you list into what portons you will, then ye number not parted multiply in euery of those parts: the summes collected declare the same whiche the two whole numbers multiplied togither woulde haue brought.   Example.

I woulde multiplie 34041 by 1110, deuide this summe 1110 in parts as 1000, 100, 10, and with euerie of them multiplie the other 342041 the nubers produced are these.

$$
\begin{array}{r}
342041000 \\
34204100 \\
3420410 \\
\hline
\end{array}
$$
Now collected

maketh 379665510

This is demonstrated in the firste Proposition of the second booke of *Euclides* Elements.

Of

Of Partition.   Chap. 5.

TO deuide or parte, is ingeniously to find how oftentimes
the diuisor is conteined in the number to be diuided, or to
part any number into as manye portions as youre diuisor
appoynteth. Then diuision sheweth onely howe often the
lesse summe is conteyned in the bigger, as if I woulde diuide 40 by 8, that declareth how oftentimes 8 is conteyned
in 40, so find I 5, and thus is my diuision perfourmed. The
lesse summe is the Diuisor or Diuidet, the other y number
to be diuided or diuisible, vnder whome, the two lines or
paralels must be drawen for your quotiet, and the Diuisor
vnder them. This kind being contrarie to Multiplication,
requireth contrarie working, that is, from the lefte, to the
right hand: your Diuisor there founde, how often he is conteyned in the number ouer him, that same Character placed
in the quotiente, and the Diuident or Diuisor in that Character found multiplyed, Subtraction made, &c. your Diuisor ought to be remoued to the next place toward the righte
hand, and so to the ende, as by example more playnely shall
appeare. I would diuide 3089 by 3, at all times sette and
order your number thus.

	0 x 2
The number to be diuided.	3 0 8 9
The Quotient.	1 0 2 9
The Diuisor.	3 3 3 3
	6

Paralels nowe drawen, and my Diuisor placed vnder
the last of my number to be diuided, whiche was 3, I finde
once 3 to be 3, whiche Subtracted from the Figure 3 right a-
boue him, nothing is left, dash 3. This one place betwéene
the lines right ouer 3. The Diuisor 3 conuey to the nexte
rowme rightward, where in the Ciphre ouer him, he is not
once found, therefore put this Ciphre o betwéene the Paralels, right ouer y Diuisor, and so remouing a place farther,
that

vnder 8, there you finde the diuident twice : wherefore, put
2 in the quotiēt right vnder 8, then say twice 3 is sire, which
subtracted from 8, leaueth 2 ouer 8 dashed. The Diuisor 3
now dashed, is conueyed to the nexte and last place, whyche
being founde 9 times in 29, put 9 in the quotient, saying, 9
times 3 maketh 27, that subducted from 29 aboue, 2 remay=
neth ouer 9, the rest dashed. Note if it chance that the Di=
uisor be conteyned oftner than 9 times, onely 9 put in the
quotient. Behold another example 19031 to be diuided in
211 partes, place them directly thus.

$$\begin{array}{r} 1\ 1\ 4 \\ \text{The number diuisible.}\quad 1\ 9\ 0\ 3\ 1 \\ \text{The Quotient.}\quad 9\quad\ \ 0\ \big|\ 41\ \textit{Remaynes.} \\ \text{The Diuisor.}\quad \overline{2\ 1\ 1\ 1}\ \big|\ 211\ \textit{Diuisor permanēt} \\ 9\ 9 \\ 2\ 1 \end{array}$$

Paralels drawen, and all things placed as the example
sheweth, bycause 2, the last of the Diuisor, is bigger than 1
the last of the number to be deuided, he hath place vnder the
nert, which is 9. 2 is conteyned in 19 nine times, therefore
put 9 in ẙ quotiēt, placed as you see vnder 9, saying 9 times
2 is 18, take that out of 19, there remayneth 1 to be set ouer
9, dashing 2 and 19 with your penne. Then 9 times one is
9, strike one, take that out of 10, ouer remayneth 1 ouer
the Ciphre, the vnite leftward put out. Now to the last of
your Diuisor, 9 times 1 is 9, dash 1, take that 9 out of 13, a=
boue remayneth 4 ouer 3, strike 13 with your penne, remoue
your Diuidente a place farther rightwarde, the rest follo=
wing leftward in order. See how oftentimes your Diuisor
may be had out of the number ouer him, that is no time, put
therefore the 0 in your quotient, dashing euery Element of
your Diuident, permitting the remaynes to be set ouer the
Diuisor, and so you haue in youre quotiente 90, there re=
maines 41. In like manner, all other numbers are diuided.

C. Vse

Vſe in this matter preuayleth, and openeth that whiche many words can not.

Diuiſion beeing but a conuerſe working, or reſolution of Multiplication, is demonſtrated by the foreledged firſte Propoſition of the ſecond Booke of the Geome‐tricall Elements.

Speedie and compendious
fashions of *Diuiſion*.

Loke howe manye Ciphres the Diuiſor hath afore the figures of ſignification, ſo manye places ſeparate by line, or cutte away at the beginning of youre number that ſhall be diuided, the reſt ſhall ſuffer partition by the Cha‐racters only ſignificatiue, as is declared with mixt Ciphres in your Diuident.

Example.

The number to be diuided, is 3454000:the Diuiſor 30200:Lo two Ciphres vnmixt in your Diuiſor, therfore two places in your nūber to be diuided muſt be cut away, then the reſt ſtand thus to be diuided.

```
                1 1
               1 3 2
             0 4 3 2 2
Diuidend.    3 4 5 4 0 | 0 0
Quotient.       1 1 4  .        | 1 1 2 0 0  Remaynes.
Diuiſor.     3 0 2 2 2          | 3 0 2 0 0  Diui.permanēt.
             3 0 2 0
                3
```

The remaynes 112 ſhall be ioyned with the Elemēts cut away and put ouer the whole Diuiſor, as aboue. This as I thinke is ſufficient for Diuiſion, more woulde rather diſ‐courage than farther.

Of Reduction. Chap. 6.

To Reduce, is to bring a number of groſſe denominati‐on into a ſmaller or contrarie. Groſſe to ſubtile by Mul‐tiplication,

tiplication, Subtile, to groſſe by partition is perfourmed. A number of groſſe Denomination is that, which conteyneth manye other ſubtiler oʒ ſmaller, as a Pounde in reſpecte of Shillings. Shillings in compariſon to Poundes are a ſubtile denomination. If you will reduce any groſſe ſumme into a ſubtiller oʒ contrarie, you muſt well ponder how many of that ſmaller do make one of the groſſer, and by that multiplie oʒ diuide, as occaſion is giuen. I woulde bʒing 600 ℔ into halfe pens. Firſte you muſt reduce them into Shillings, multiplying by 20. Then augment the Pʒoduct by 12, ſo be pʒoduced pens, and foʒ halfe pens multiplie the ſurmounting number by 2. The whole ſumme reduced, ſtandeth thus 288000 halfe pens. Nowe by partition this ſubtile ſumme is bʒought to his foʒmer eſtate, that is, 600 ℔. In like maner, a Mile in reſpect of Furlongs, Furlongs copared to ſcoʒes, Scoʒes to pearches, Pearches to yards, Pards to féete, Féete to ynches, Ynches to Barlie coʒnes referred, be of groſſe Denomination. But Barlie coʒnes to ynches, Ynches in reſpecte to féete, and ſo vpwarde, haue a ſubtile Denomination.

Our Engliſh mile grounded vpon the Statute, hath oʒdeyned thʒée barlie coʒnes dʒie and round to make an ynch, twelue ynches a foote, thʒée foote a yard, fiue yards a pearch, e foʒtie pearches in legth, e four of bʒeadth, an acre of land: ſo the acre conteyneth 160 pearches, the halfe 80, and the yarde, whiche is the quarter 40.   Twentie yards make a Scoʒe, and foʒtie pearches a Furlog, 8 furlong a Mile. So that by Reduction, you may find in the Engliſhe mile 320 pearches, 1760 yards, 5280 foote, e 63360 ynches, ſomewhat greater than y Italian mile of 1000 pace, e 5 foote to a pace.

Of waight according to the Statute of *England*.

The Engliſh Pennie which is called the Sterling round without clipping, ſhal wey 22 graines of wheat dʒy, e in y middſt of y eare. 20 pens maketh 1 ounce, 12 ounces maketh a pound, a pounde, and this weight is called *Troy* weighte, whiche Goldsmithes commonly vse. By this whiche is saide, you may gather the ounce to conteine 4 4 0 graynes of wheate, and the pound 5 2 8 0. There is another moze vsuall weight called *Haberdepoyse*, the Scruple conteyneth 20 Graynes of Barlie, as the Pennie of *Troy*, the Dramme 3 scruples, the ounce 8 Drammes, so ye maye perceyue 4 8 0 Graynes of Barlie in the ounce, and 7 6 8 0 in a pound: but these rates often alter.

Of Progreſſion, or rather of moſt com-
pendious Addition. Chap. 7.

PRogreſſion is a very compendious way to knitte and gather in one those numbers which do proceede with an eauen and equal diſtance. In all Arithmetical Progreſſion, you ſhall conioyne the extreames, augmenting the number of those extreames so added, with the number that sheweth how many places there be in the whole round of your progreſſion, the product mediating, as 5. 10. 20. 25. 30. 35. By adding the extreames whiche is 5, and 35, encreaseth 40, multiplie it by the places which is 7, riseth 2 8 0, diuided by 2, oz mediated, sheweth 140 the whole summe. There is another kinde of Progreſſion, named Geometricall, whyche encreaseth by 2,3,4,5,oz mofold infinitely, behold y figure.

$$\left\{\begin{array}{cccc} 1 & 2 & 4 & 8 \\ 2 & 6 & 18 & 54 \\ 3 & 15 & 75 & 375 \end{array}\right\} \left\langle\begin{array}{c} 2 \\ 3 \\ 4 \end{array}\right.$$

I call it fiuefold, when the firſte number may be founde iuſt 5 times in the next summe, and so of the reſt. For these and all other like, multiplie the laſt number by that it folded, subtracting the firſt from the product, continually diuiding by one leſſe, than the doubling oz folding is. Example 1, 2, 4, 8, 16, 32, 64, this number foldeth by 2, therefore multiplie the laſt 64 by 2, which maketh 12 8. Subtracte 1,
the

the firſte figure, ſo remayneth 127, that diuided by one leſſe
than the folding agayne 127 riſeth, the whole ſumme of
your Progreſſion. Note if you multiplie the laſt, oz any o-
ther place of Geometricall Pzogreſſion (beginning wyth
an Unite) with himſelfe, the pzoduct ſheweth as many mo
places ſaue one. Example. I woulde haue the fourtéenth
place, oz rœme of the Pzogreſſion immediately aboue
wzitten, 64 the laſt number of that pzopoztion, declareth 7
rœmes oz places, and in hymſelfe multiplyed, bzingeth
4096 the thirtéenth place, now multiplie by 2, with which
it foulded, ſo haue you 8192, the fourtéenth rœme your deſire, foz the true value of all, do as is afozeſaid of Geometricall Pzogreſſion.

The finding of Rootes of ſquare
numbers. Chap. 8.

TO find the ſquare *Radix*, oz Rœte of any number, is to
gather a ſumme that multiplyed in himſelfe, if it be
quadzate, iuſtly may make the afozeſayde number, oz elſe
it may engender the bigger ſquares ſumme in that conteyned. A ſquare number is that which reſulteth of any number once multiplyed in himſelfe. A quadzate *Radix* is called that number, whiche by himſelfe multiplyed, yéeldeth a
ſquare ſumme. To quadzate oz to augment ſquarely, is to
encreaſe any number with himſelfe, as four times 4, maketh 16, it followeth 16 to be a ſquare number, and 4 of that
ſumme the rœte oz *Radix*, euen ſo of al other. A ſquare number deuiſed by vnites, maketh a quadzate Figure as appeareth.

Bycauſe

Bycause the Quadrate roote differeth little from Diuision (for it is as it were a kinde of Partition) it needeth not many wordes, you shall beginne so worke as in that kinde, that is, from the left hand to the right, putting downe your numbers, separating euerie two elements from the beginning with pendente or hanging lines, drawing also two Paralels vnder them for your quotiente.

Example.

I would haue the *Radix* of 3969, place and handle youre numbers thus.

	c		
	o 3	o o	
The number proposed.	3 9	6 9	
The Roote Q.	6	3	
The double numbers	3 6 x 9		
of the Rootes.	1 6		
	3		

You shall search for a number, which multiplyed in himselfe, may consume as nigh as may be 39, being the two firste figures leftwards separated by line, which is 6, put him betweene the Paralels vnder 9. Then saye sixe times 6 is 36, take it out of 39, so remayneth 3, to be written ouer 9. This done, double your Quotient 6, which maketh 12. That doubled number ought to be set vnder the Paralels, the firste 2 vnder 6, the next 1 vnder 9. Again, you ought to find a number, which multiplyed in ÿ said double, shal wast the summe leftwarde, and directly aboue it in the head: you may find ÿ number to be 3, which you must put in the Quotient vnder 9, the next place following the double. Note your Radicall Digites found, must be placed vnder the elemente nexte to the pendent lines. Then say, three times twelue maketh 36. After you haue take 36 from 36 dashed in the head, you shall multiplie 3 the last found nuber of the Quotient in it selfe, & take it out of the numbers ouer. This done, the number is perceyued to be square, because nothing remayneth. The

Qua

Quadrate roote being 36. Whē it ſhal chance that you may
not find a ſumme, which multiplyed in the double number,
and after in himſelfe may be takē out of the head, then you
ſhal go foꝛth, ⁊ ſet down this Ciphꝛe o, doubling your quotient as afoꝛe. Héere followeth another Example, woꝛke it
foꝛ your exerciſe.

Note this oftentimes, the number aboue the double is ſo
great, that it troubleth beginners much to know what Digit will ſerue. Therefoꝛe diuide the numbers leftward, and
aboue the double, with the double it ſelfe, the Quotient wil
declare very nigh the Digit to be put betwene the lines. If
you require exactneſſe, ſée whether the reſidue of that which
is left of Diuiſion, with the Character of the Element, vnder whome the Digit muſt be put, be bigger oꝛ equall in
number with the Digit himſelfe multiplyed: if it be the
leſſe, the Digit muſt be diminiſhed one Vnite oꝛ two at the
moſt. Alſo note, the remaynes ſhall haue his name of the
Radix doubled, adding to it an vnite.

Another ſubtile way to find this *Radix.*

TO any nūber, whoſe Roote you require, adde rightward
ſo many Ciphꝛes as you liſt, ſo they be euē, as oo, oooo,
oꝛ oooooo. Of that which reſulteth, ſéeke the Quadrate
Roote as we haue afoꝛe declared, not regarding the Remnant. Take from that *Radix* found, ſo many elemēts as the
number of halfe the Ciphꝛes afoꝛe added, the other toward
the left hand kéepe foꝛ the integers of your Roote: multiplie
the elements taken by what article number you liſt, euen
as you will haue the parts of the whole come, as by 10, 30,
60, ⁊c. from the Pꝛoduct pull ſo many elements as halfe the
afoꝛeſaid added Ciphꝛes, the reſt ẏ remayneth, wꝛite beſide
the

the integers of your rote, as a Fraction, whose name (of the article) he must haue by whome he was multiplyed, and thus procéde, till you haue all Ciphers, yea so many, as halfe the afore added. The more Ciphers you put at the beginning, the more preciser your rote shall be. Héere néedeth no example, if all things aboue written be vnderstode.

The finding of the Cubicall
roote or *Radix*.

To search or pull out the *Radix*, or rote cubical, is to get a summe multiplyed once by himself, and again in the Product engendring the number proponed if it be Cubicall. A number Cubicall is that whiche by multiplication in hymselfe, and agayne in that surmounteth, is ingendred. *Radix* or Rote Cubicall, is that number so multiplyed, making the said summe cubicall. To multiplie anye number cubicallye, is to encrease it once in himselfe, and againe that number with the product, as if I woulde multiplie 4, 4 in himselfe maketh 16, and foure times 16, is 64. A solidate cubicall figure, is imagined with sire square *Superficies* or sides like a Dye, as this Figure sheweth.

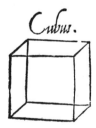

Cubus.

The searching of the rote Cubicall, is not very vnlike to the finding of the quadrate rote, this first excepted, that the Figures must be put downe, euery thirde separated from

from the beginning with hanging lines: beholde the Example.

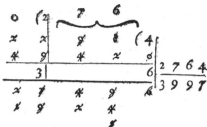

The number propoſed.
Radix Cubicall.
The tripled Rootes.

All things well diſpoſed as is ſaide, nowe J muſt ſéeke a number multiplyed in himſelfe cubicallp, whiche may take away as nigh as maye be 49 : 4 is too muche, 3 will ſerue. Put downe 3 in your Quotient vnder 9 next to the pendent line rightwarde, multiplying him cubicallp, the Product 27 ſubducting from 49, remapneth 22 ouer their heads. Then triple 3, ſetting the Producte vnder the nexte elemente ſaue one, from the Digit laſt found rightwarde, whiche is there vnder 2, and the other following in order leftwarde if there be mo. Note oftentimes as it is ſaid in the ſquare, the number aboue the thréefold leftward is ſo bigge, that with eaſe the Radical Digit can not be found. Therefore ſuppoſe this o to be betwéene your Paralels in ſtead of poure Digitte, a roome beponde all the thréefold rightwarde. The reſulting then of your Quotiente increaſe bp the thréefolde number, and with the ſumme that ſurmounteth, diuide the Characters aboue the thréefold and ſo leftwarde, the Quotiente of that partition appeareth to be the Digit, ſo that the remain of that diuiſion, iopned with the element, vnder whome the Digit muſt be put, be more or equall compared with the cubicall multiplication of the laſt founde digit. Otherwiſe 1 or 2 leſſe at the moſt will ſerue. The next digit on this wiſe founde, being hére 6, let him be augmented togither with the firſt in the thréefold number 9, thus 36 in 9, maketh 324, and the ſame againe with the laſt found digit multiplyed,

D. ſo

so haue you 1944 to be subtracted from aboue the thræfolde 9, and so leftward, whiche number is 2242, then remayneth 298, the figure 8 to be set ouer the head of 2. This 6 the last Digit founde, and so all other, must be placed immediatelp (when it is searched out) euer a place farther betwéene the Parallels rightward than any figure of your double, that is at all times vnder the Element nexte to the Pendente line. Now multiplie 6 Cubically, which is 216 to be Subtracted from the Characters aboue him and leftward, so remaineth 2764, wherefore the number wroughte, is not Cubicall. Note when your Vnite is to much to be put in your Quotiente, then let this Ciphre o take place, and so procéde to the ende, tripling as afore all youre Radicall Digittes. This whyche is sayde, sufficeth for all manner numbers, much vse rather than many wordes is hére required.

Another precise vvay for the finding
of this Cubicall Roote.

A Dde towarde the righte hande as is sayde in numbers square to any summe so manye Ciphres as you list, so that those added Ciphres may be diuided in thrée partes equally, as 000, or 000, 000, or else 000, 000, 000, that is 3 at the least 6 or 9. Of the number that surmounteth, take the Cubicall Roote, as aboue is sayde, the Remaynes nothing regarding. Pull away toward the righte hande so many Elemēts as the third part of the afore added Ciphres amounte to, the other leftwarde kéepe as the Integers of your *Radix*. Nowe with these Elementes pulled away, worke as is sayde in numbers square in the seconde finding, euer cutting away toward the right hand so many elements as the third part of the afore added. Better it is, if you worke still by one Article.

Hovv

Hovv the Denominator is founde to
the *Remayes* Cubicall.

You ſhall firſte ſquare your Cubicall *Radix*, that ſquare triple, Triple alſo ẙ *Radix*. Adde theſe triples togither, adioyning 1 to the reſulting ſumme, maketh the Denominatoʒ.

Oʒ multiplie the *Radix* in the triple of an number, one Unite bigger than the ſaid *Radix*, and to the pʒoduct of that Multiplication, adioyne an Unite, ſo haue you the deſired Denominatoʒ.

Oʒ adde an Unite to your *Radix*, and encreaſe the reſulting ſumme by your Roote Cubicall, this pʒoduct triple, and adde thereto an vnitie, ſo ariſeth the Denominatoʒ alſo.

This Denominator ſhal be placed vnder a ſtreight line, dʒawen at the right hand of your Quotiente, as in the laſt Example you maye behold. Then ſet ouer the ſame the remayne of your Roote, ſo haue you a Fraction, whoſe nature you ſhall immediately know.

The prooues of all the kindes
afore mentioned. Chap. 10.

The contrarie kind is ẙ true examinatiõ of ẙ other, as by

{ *Addition*	{ *Subductiõ*	{ *Multipli.*	{ *Augmentation*	} *is proued.*
Subtractiõ	*Collection*	*Diuiſion*	*Partition.*	

Although this ſuffice foʒ bʒeuitie, yet I ſhall at large put foʒth the pʒoues.

After you haue added your numbers togither, pull out any ſumme oʒ row there conteyned, the other ſummes not ſubtracted, ſhall remayne, if you haue well done.

Adde the numbers which you did ſubtrahe vnto the Pʒoduct, and it ſhall be equall to the firſt ſumme.

D.ÿ.   Diuide

Diuide the Producte eyther by the Multiplycator, oz the number to be multiplyed, and the other part sheweth hymselfe.

Multiplie the Quotient with the Diuisoz. If the number that surmounteth with the rest remayning, make your number that was diuided, you haue rightly done.

When grosse into subtile is broughte, Diuision by the Multiplicator bringeth the greate former summe. Subtile in grosse wrought in like manner, Multiplicatiō proueth it.

Out of the whole summe gathered, subtract euery number in the row, the last subducted, nothing shall remayne.

The Roote oz *Radix* in himselfe must be multiplyed, and if there be any thing left, let it be added to the Producte, so haue you the first summe.

Euen so the Cubicall *Radix*, augmented in himselfe cubically, adding the remaynes, yeeldeth the former summe.

The false proofes by nines, Multiplication in squares, Diuisions peculiar to one forged diuidente, accompting by Counters, and such like, are heere omitted, bycause they doe rather trouble, yea lade wittes than profite.

Thus endeth the first part, teaching the supputation of Integers, and heere followeth the second of Fractions.

The expressing of the vulgare or common *Fractions*. Chap. 12.

A Fraction is a Distribution, appointed of a part oz parts of an Integer. As the Integers take their beginning at 1, and continue in number without ende, euen so the said Integers, by imagination from one second part, maye be dissolued, oz broken in portions oz parts infinite. The partes of those simple oz principall Fractions, haue also to them parts following. To atteyne the knowledge of them, acquaynte your selfe with these two termes, Numerator, and Denominator. The office and duetie of the first, is, to

expresse

expresse the number of such parts. The Denominator doth giue to those parts their names, as $\frac{3}{4}$ which is thrée portiõs of a thing diuided in 4. The Numerator is called the Elementes or Figures that be alway set aboue the short line. The Characters or Elements vnder, beare the name of the Denominator. The Numerator is at all times first pronounced, as $\frac{2}{3}$ $\frac{3}{4}$ $\frac{1}{5}$ as two thirdes, thrée fourthes, one fifte. Simple or principall Fractions be euer as afore written, but fragmentes of Fractions thus, $\frac{2}{4}$ $\frac{1}{5}$ $\frac{1}{6}$ and numbred on this wise, two fourths of one fift, of one sixt: note these Fractions following $\frac{4}{4}$ $\frac{10}{9}$ $\frac{2}{3}$. The last being leftwarde, maketh one whole, the Numerator being as much as the Denominator, the other following, giueth one Integer , and one ninth, the Numerator excéeding the Denominator by the ninth part. The third wãteth one Unite to create a whole, the Numerator being destitute of one third. The bigger the Denominator, the further the Fractions are from the whole. In Supputation, there doth assemble and runne togither numbers both greate and small, whole and broken, principall Fractions, with Integers and Fragmentes of Fractions. Therefore of necessitie to auoyde confusion, I must first declare how to reduce these diuers kindes into one fashion or likenesse.

Of Reduction in Fractions.

Chapter. 12.

TO reduce, is to bring Integers into Fractions or contrarie, yea a fragment or Fractions of diuers Denominations into one, or what name you list. You shall reduce integers or whole, into what parte you will, multiplying the integers by the denomination of those partes, as if I would breake 8 whole in thirdes, multiply 8 by 3, riseth $\frac{24}{3}$. If I would bring 5 integers and $\frac{3}{4}$ into one name, I must multiplye the Integers into the Denominatoz 4, adding to the Product 3, so haue yée $\frac{23}{4}$. To reduce partes oz fractions into whole, diuide the Numeratoz of those fractions by the Denominatoz, as $\frac{25}{4}$ diuided by 4 proceedeth 6 Integers & $\frac{1}{4}$ of an whole . The remaines euer acknowledge their name of the Diuisor, and beare the propoztion to the whole (oz Integer) of the Numeratoz to the Denominatoz, whiche was Diuisoz. When ye will change great partes into the lesse oz contrarp, yée shal multiply the Numeratoz of it that you entended to chaunge, into the Denominatoz of it, into whom yée will make the change, and whatsoeuer resulteth you shal deuide by the Denominatoz of it that yée began to chaunge, so haue yée those partes which yée required, risen out of the Diuision.

Example.

I would reduce $\frac{5}{8}$ into seauenthes, augmente 5 into 7 encreaseth 35, diuided by 8 sheweth in Partition 4, and 3 the remayn which significth $\frac{3}{8}$ $\frac{7}{}$, so of $\frac{5}{8}$ bzought into seauenthes commeth $\frac{4}{7}$ and $\frac{3}{8}$ of one seauenth parte . Whensoeuer in suche Reduction there is lefte anye remayne after the Diuision made, it is a fragment of a fraction and shal take his name in the Nominatiue case of the Denominatoz of that whiche is the Diuisoz, and receyue hys other name in the oblique case of the Denominatoz into whom the change oz reduction is made. Fragments of fractions be thus bzought into pzincipall fractions. Multiply the Numeratozs in themselues fozging one common Numeratoz . Also the Denominatozs by themselues , causing one Denominatoz in common, as $\frac{2}{7}$ $\frac{1}{2}$ $\frac{1}{2}$ so reduced bzingeth $\frac{4}{70}$ of one Integer . To reduce two fractions to one pzincipall fragmente multiplye the one Denominatoz by the other, so haue yée pzoduced a common Denominatoz . Then multiplye the Numeratoz of the one fraction into the Denominatoz of the other , and againe the Denominatoz of the other fragment into the Numeratoz of the
first

firſte, adding the Productes togyther whiche ſhall be a
Numerator in common. As thus ⅔ and ¼. Multiply as aboue
is ſayde 3 in 4 that is 12 the common Denominator, then 2
the firſt Numerator augmented in 4 maketh 8. Put that 8
aboue ⅔, then multiply 5 the Numerator of the ſecond Fra=
ction in 3 increaſeth 15, the whiche note ouer ¼. Theſe pecu=
liar Numerators added togither, riſeth 23. Wright ouer the
12 after this faſhion 23/12 ſo ⅔ and ¼ make 23/12 of the which 8 bée
made of ⅔ and 15 of ¼. Beholde

The Example.

$$\left\{ \begin{array}{ccc} \frac{8}{} & \frac{15}{} & \\ \frac{2}{3} & \frac{1}{4} & \frac{23}{12} \end{array} \right\}$$

Manye and diuerſe Fractions on this wiſe be brought
to one ſimple Fraction. After yée haue produced two of the
firſte Fragmentes as aboue, then multiplie the common
Denominator (firſt reduced) into the Denominator of the
nexte Fraction to be reduced. Of that riſeth a Denomi=
nator in common. Nowe for youre Numerator worke
thus.

Yée ſhal multiply the Numerator of the firſt reduced in=
to the Denominator of the thirde, whiche is to be reduced,
and contrarie the Denominator of the Reduct into the Nu=
merator of the laſt Fragment to be reduced, ſo by Additi=
on yée ſhall haue a Numerator in common, euen thus of all
Fractions howe manye ſoeuer they are. The firſt alwayes
diſpatched, adioyne the nexte, vntill yée haue pervſed them
thorowly.

Example.

⅔ ¾ ½. After yée haue reduced the 2 firſte thus 23/12 adioyne
to him the next on this wiſe, 23/12 ½. Nowe multiplye the De=
nominators, commeth 24 the common Denominator.
                                                    Then

Then 23 by 2 encreaseth 46, and 12 by one multiplyed yéeldeth 12, 46 and 12 added make 58 the Numeratoz in common.
Thus standeth youre Fractions aboue written, reduced $\frac{58}{24}$
which contain 2 integers, and $\frac{10}{24}$ oz $\frac{1}{12}$ of one integer. Marke
wel if integers, fractions, and fragments of fractions shall
fortune to come togither, bzing them all to pzincipall fragments as aboue is declared, that done, perfozme euery thing
by the rules afozesayde.

The Abbreuiation of Fractions.
Chap. 13.

TO abbreuiate any Fragment, is to bzing a Fraction to
his lest denomination. To make this abbzeuiation, yée
must diuide the Numeratoz of the Fraction, and so in the
like maner the Denominatoz by the biggest number, that is
some common part of them both. The Quotient by diuision
of the Numeratoz, sheweth the Numeratoz of the Fraction
abbzeuiated. Likewise by partition of the Denominatoz
his Fragment in the Quotient appeareth.

Example.

I woulde abbzeuiate $\frac{4}{12}$ deuide 4, the Numeratoz by 4,
which 4 so appeareth 1. Now 12 deuided by that 4 ariseth 3,
foz the Denominatoz, which also haue place thus $\frac{1}{3}$, béyng
the least Denomination. This big number is founde by diuiding the Nominator, with the Numeratoz of the Fraction. If nothing be left of that partition, the Numeratoz oz
Diuisoz is that great number as afoze. When any thing remayneth, with that diuide the number that afoze yée made
your Diuisoz, and thus continue on til nothing remaine, so
your last Diuident is that gret number which serueth your
tourne. In case by often Partition your last Diuisoz cometh
to an Unite, thé those fractions oz numbers be called *Contra*
se Primi, and may not be reduced to any lower name.

How

Hovv to knovv the value of remnants that be
left by Diuision of Integers or whole.

TO make ſhort worke, reduce the Integer into the moſte ſubtile Denomination that to him belongeth, then multiply that reduction by the Numerator of the Fraction, and diuide by the Denominator of the ſayde Fragment, the quotient vttereth the value of the parts or Fractions. Here needeth no example.

Of Addition. Chap. 14.

TO ad in common Fractiõs, is to gather and reduce many Fragmentes to one ſumme or principal Fraction. This is ſufficiently entreated of before. Notwithſtanding I ſhal not ſpare here ſomewhat to ſay. If your Fraction bée of one Denomination, then gather or adde the Numerators togither, ſubſcribing the Denominator, as $\frac{2}{4}\frac{3}{4}\frac{4}{4}$ maketh $\frac{9}{4}$ which is 2 hole, and $\frac{1}{4}$, but being diuerſe and vnlike, multiply the Numerators by the Denominators croſſe wayes, adding them togither, ſo haue yée a common Numerator, to whom ſubſcribe a Denominator common.

Example.

$\frac{2}{3}$ and $\frac{5}{8}$ produce $\frac{31}{24}$ to the whiche yée may adde $\frac{1}{4}$ that maketh a $\frac{117}{96}$, being 3 hole, and $\frac{1}{4}$. Note if Integers and Fractions ſhall accompany togither, firſt adde the Integers, after the Fractions, & if the Fragments may create an Integer, adioyne them to the other whole.

Of Subduction. Chap. 15.

SVbduction is the taking of the one Fraction from the other, the leſſo from the greater, or equal from the like or equall. Those Fractions be named the greater, whose Numerator multiplyed in the Denominator of ye other, engendreth the greater number. Subtrahe $\frac{3}{4}$ from $\frac{7}{4}$ remayneth $\frac{4}{4}$, whiche is one whole. When the Denominators be diuerse as $\frac{4}{5}$ from $\frac{3}{2}$. Multiply 5 with 2 cometh 10 the common Denominator to be set vnder. Then foure times 2 yeeldeth 8. In like manner three times 5 bringeth 15. Nowe Subtract 8 from 15, remayneth 7, the which hath place thus, $\frac{7}{10}$. When yee woulde Subtrahe $\frac{3}{4}$ from 4 Integers and $\frac{1}{2}$, the last Fraction being lesse then $\frac{3}{4}$, enforceth you to Subtrahe one out of 4, resoluing him into seconds, and adioyned to the other so haue ye $\frac{3}{2}$, from whome take $\frac{3}{4}$ remayneth $\frac{6}{8}$, abbreuiated $\frac{3}{4}$, to whome adioyne 3 whole, it standeth thus, $3\frac{3}{4}$. If yee list to take 6 and $\frac{2}{3}$ out of 8 and $\frac{3}{4}$ the Integres being reduced into their proper Fragments, make your Subduction as aboue is sayd, so remayneth 2 and $\frac{1}{12}$ of an whole.

Of Multiplication. Chap. 16.

MVltiply the Numerators togither in themselues, then the Denominators, so haue yee both a Numerator and a Denominator in common.

Example.

$\frac{2}{3}$ $\frac{3}{4}$ and $\frac{1}{2}$ by $\frac{4}{5}$, Two times 3 maketh 6, once 6 yeeldeth 6 whiche multiplyed in 4 bringeth 24, the common Numerator. Then three times 4 increaseth 12, that augmented in 2 engendreth 24 and so in 5 surmounteth 120, the Denominator in common, which all standeth thus, $\frac{24}{120}$, but abbreuiated in this wise, $\frac{1}{5}$. Three Integers by $\frac{2}{3}$ or contrarie be thus multiplyed, 2 the Numerator of the Fraction multiplyed in 3 bringeth 6, which 6 must be written ouer the Denominator of the Fragment thus $\frac{6}{3}$ or 2 Integers. Integers by multiplycation growe both in quantitye and number, the Fraction

tion increaseth onlye in number and diminisheth in quantity. Note when whole be ioyned with simple Fractions, only oz with Integers coupled with Fragmentes, oz else contrarie, Reduce the Integers and ioyne them to their proper
Fraction, and after multiplye them accozding to the Arte of
Fragments.

Of Partition. Chap. 17.

IF your Fractions be of one Denomination, diuide as
in Integers, putting the remaines ouer the diuisoz. I
would diuide by $\frac{6}{4}\frac{8}{4}$ the quotient bzingeth fozth 1 whole, and
$\frac{2}{8}$. Let your Diuisor be euer placed on the left side. When the
Denominatozs be vnlike, ye shall multiplye crosse-wise as
by $\frac{2}{3}$ diuide $\frac{4}{8}$. Augment 3 in 4 there commeth 12 the Nominator, the 8 by 2 riseth 16 the Denominator, they haue place
thus $\frac{12}{16}$ and abbzeuiated on this wise $\frac{3}{4}$. When Integers
commeth to be diuided by simple oz pzincipall Fractions oz
contrarie, the Integers ought to be set aboue the line after
the manner of Fragmentes putting vnder the Vnite, the
Diuident (as I haue sayde) occupying the lefte side. Nowe
wozke as aboue yée haue learned in diuision of Fractions.

Example.

By $\frac{5}{7}$ deuide $\frac{1}{6}$ riseth $\frac{7}{10}$, abbzeuiated thus $\frac{7}{10}$. Another example by $\frac{2}{3}$, parte $\frac{5}{4}$ so commeth $\frac{15}{2}$ whiche is 7 Integers
and $\frac{1}{2}$.

If Integers with pzincipall Fractions yea oz Fragmentes
of Fractions come to be diuided by Integers oz whole whyche be accompanied with simple, bzoken, oz Fractions of
Fragmentes, when these bzoken are reduced to a simple
Fragment, and the Integers to the same kinde that his ioyned Fraction is of. Then perfozme your Partition as afoze
is sayde.

Of the Quadrate roote. Chap. 18.

Fyée may, take the Quadrate roote both of the Numerator and Denominator, as in the Integers: for example thus, of $\frac{4}{9}$ the Quadrat roote is $\frac{2}{3}$. Now followeth a generall waye for all manner of fractions.

Suppose a number and multiplye it with the Denominator of youre fraction the produce shall be the Denominator of the *Radix*. Then for your Numerator, multiplye the number afore supposed in himselfe, and that whiche redoundeth augment in the Denominator of the Fraction, the product multiplye in the Numerator of the fragmente, then of that mounting summe, take the Roote as is said in the eight Chapter of this first booke, which is the Radix of the Numerator. Now place them one ouer the other abbreuiating if néede be. The example of the Cubicall roote following, maketh this which I haue sayd, manifest.

Of the Cubicall roote. Chap. 19.

For the Cubical roote worke thus. Example $\frac{12}{23}$ let your number supposed be 6, with it multiply 29 riseth 174 the Denominator. Now increase 6 in himselfe Cubically commeth 216, which augmented with 29 bringeth 6264, the product, again multiplyed by 29 engendereth this summe 181656 whiche to conclude, multiplyed in the Numerator of youre fraction, surmounteth this 1816560. Nowe the *Radix* cubicall founde (as is mentioned in the ninth Chapter of this booke) sheweth your Numerator which is 122. Put your Denominator vnder him thus, $\frac{122}{174}$ abbreuiated maketh $\frac{2}{3}$ and $\frac{2}{62}$ of an whole. Thus get the Cubical roote of al other fractions.

Of

Of the Rule of Proportion, commonly called the Golden Rule.
Chapter 20.

His Rule is also called the Rule of thzee, foz as muche as by thzee pzopoztionall numbers knowen, it alwaye searcheth out the fourth pzopoztionall, as if nine paices of Ueluet cost eleuen poundes, what shall 33 of the same cost. Héere are thzée numbers giuen, and a fourth demaunded. Foz the resolution of this and all suche like, wozke by the Rule ensuing.

The Rule.

Multiplie the last number by the seconde, and diuide the Pzoduct by the first number, so will your Quotient and remayne discouer the fourth pzopoztionall desired.

{ *The Demonstration of this Rule is grounded on the 19 Propo-sition of the seauenth Booke of the Geometricall Elements.*

Example.

I multiplie 33 by 11, there ariseth 363, whiche diuided by 9, yéeldeth in the Quotient 40, and in the remayne $\frac{1}{3}$, whych reduced, maketh $\frac{1}{3}$, I conclude therfoze 33 yards of the same Ueluet shall cost foztie Pounds, and a Noble.

{ *If 9 yards of Veluet coste* } 11 *Poundes,* { *33 yardes wyll coste* } 40 $\frac{1}{3}$ *Poundes*

But in placing of the thzée numbers this must be obserued, that the first and third be of one Denomination, as in this question they are both Veluet, and that the numbers pzoponed foz a paterne, be first placed, and the number, whose fellowe you séeke, be alwayes placed last. Héere I tearme first and last, accozding to our vsuall maner of wziting from the left hande to the right, and not as in Numeration.

E.iij. The

The Rule of Proportion
Inuerſed.

THe Rule is termed Inuerſed, when the queſtion is ſo propouned, that according to the courſe of the numbers, the fourth ſhoulde ſurmount the thirde, and yet in reaſon it muſt in deede be leſſe, or contrariwiſe by courſe of numbers diminiſhing, when it ought to encreaſe : As if twelue Maſons be able to make a certayne wall in twentie dayes, how many ſhall make the ſame in fiue dayes.

{ The numbers }
{ in order placed } *If 20 Dayes giue 12 Men, what yeldeth 5 Days.*

Heere it is apparante, that by the courſe of theſe numbers, as 12 is leſſe than 20, ſo the fourth ſoughte ſhoulde be leſſe than fiue, and therefore conſequently muche leſſe than 12 dayes, but reaſon teacheth me, that if twelue men be 20 dayes about a peece of worke, to diſpatche the ſame in leſſe time, it behoueth me to haue more than twelue men. The courſe of numbers therefore, and the trouth in reaſon being repugnant, I muſt worke by the Rule of proportió inuerſed. That is, to multiplie the firſte by the ſecond, and diuide by the third.

Example.

20 multiplied by 12, produceth 240, which diuided by fiue, yeldeth 48. So many men I ſay are to bee employed to finiſh the wall in fiue dayes, and therefore the Queſtion reſolued, ſtandeth thus :

{ If 20 Dayes bee   { the worke by 12 Men, then to finiſh it in fiue
{ required to finiſh { Dayes, you muſt prouide 48 Men.

The

The Golden Rule double
wrought.

SOmetime queſtions are proponed, wherein the Rule of Proportion muſt be twice wrought, before the queſtion can be reſolued. As if fiue Cannons at a batterie ſpende 60 Barrels of Powder in two dayes, how much Powder will ſuffiſe for fouretéene Cannons for fiue dayes. Their numbers you muſt diſpoſe in order as followeth, ſo as the firſte and laſt be alwayes in euery operation of one Denomination.

$$\left\{ \begin{array}{l} \textit{If fiue Canons ſpend 60 Barels, what ſhall 14 Canons.} \\ \textit{If two Dayes require 168 Barels, what ſhall 5 Dayes.} \end{array} \right.$$

Thus you ſée the firſt and laſt in eyther row of numbers, to aunſwere in Denomination. In the firſt Cannons. In the other Dayes: And of your fiue numbers proponed, thrée placed in the firſt row, and two in the ſecōd, leauing a ſpace in the middeſt for the fourth proportionall to be found thus. I multiplie as before is taught 14 in 60, ariſeth 840, whych deuided by 5, yéeldeth for the fourth proportionall 168, whiche I place for the ſeconde or middle number in the ſecond row, and then multiplie agayne 168 by 5, ſo haue 840, which diuided by two, yéeldeth in the Quotient 420, ſo manie Barrels of Powder will ſuffiſe fouretéene Canons for fiue dayes Batterie.

I forbeare in this place farther to entreate of the appliance of this Rule, whoſe vſe ſhall in many Militare queſtions heereafter be declared. And for that my chiefe intētion in this Treatiſe is to ſhew how *Arithmetike* maye ſtande a Souldioure in ſtead, I forbeare to intreate of the Rules of Alligation, and falſe poſitions, as thyngs friuolous for that purpoſe, and meane onely to open ſo muche of the Arte of *Algebra*, and firſte *Æquations*, as ſhall to that ende bée requiſite , reſeruing the more
exqui-

exquiſite handling of the curious *Cubicall Æquations*, and
ſecret Demonſtrations of that Arte, to be a peculiar treatiſe, wherein I will proſecute the methode of *Cardanus* in
his tenth Booke, and ſupplie (God ſparing life) the imperfections thereof.

Héere enſueth the ſeconde Booke, teaching all theſe Arithmeticall kindes in numbers Denominate, commonly called
Coſsicall, with certayne new Characters, inuented and practiſed by my Father, for the more ſpéedie diſpatch in the
wo2king of ſupputations Algebraicall. It conteyneth alſo certayne Æquations neceſſarie to be
knowen, for the reſolution of ſuch Militarie queſtions, as in the end of
the ſame Booke are adioy-
ned, touching ẙ chiefe
officers of the
fielde.

The seconde Booke.

¶ A briefe Treatise of that part of Algebra that concerneth Cossicall, or *Denominate Numbers.*

CHAP. I.

S in common Arithmetike all Abstract numbers take theïr originall from the Vnite, so in these kinde of concrete oʒ Denominate numbers, wée take oure beginning from a *Radix* oʒ Roote, not impʒoperlie so tearmed, sithens out of the same, as from the verie base and roote are deriued infinite bʒaunches of these Cossicall numbers. And as in common numbers wée pʒocéede from the Vnite by Addition, to create all kinde of Numbers, so in this Arte of Numbers Cossicall, wée pʒocéede from the Roote by Multiplication, to create all Squares, Cubes, Zenzizenzike, and Surd Solides, wyth all other that in this Science are vsed, the whyche by Example maye best bée explained.

1	2	3	4	5	6	7	8	9	10	11	12
Roo.	Sq.	Cu.	SqS.	Sso.	SqC.	Bss.	SSSq.	CC.	Sss.	Css.	SSC.
2	4	8	16	32	64	128	256	512	1024	2048	4096

Any Number Abstract may bée a Roote, and accoʒding to the value and quantitie thereof, all the other Cossicke Numbers in value and quantitie alter. Foʒ Example sake, I do héere suppose the Roote 2, the whiche multiplyed in it selfe, maketh 4 his Square, with his Character ouer hys

E. head,

head, that *Sq.* augmented agayne in his Roote, maketh 8 his Cube, and his Character ouer his head. Of these are all the reſt componed. Fo2 the Square being four, againe ſqua-red,maketh his Squared ſquare 16,with his Character ouer him. The nexte being not made by the Square o2 Cubike, Multiplication of any of the fo2mer, can not take his name from Square o2 Cube, and is therefo2e called a Surd ſolide, and is onely created by Multiplicatió of 2 the Roote, in 16 the *SqS.*making 32 with his cóuenient Character ouer him, & fo2 diſtinctió is tearmed ŷ firſt Surd ſolide. Again, 8 being the *Cu.*ſquared,maketh 64,the next number enſuing in Ge-ometricall Progreſsion,with his Character componed of *Sq.* and *Cu.* called a Squared Cube, the nexte being 128, is not made of Square o2 Cubike Multiplication of any, but only by the Multiplication of the Squared Cube in his Roote, and therefo2e is tearmed the B.S.ſolide, o2 ſeconde S.ſolide.

Héereof you maye collecte this Rule vniuerſall, to giue name to any of theſe Coſsicke Solides, conſider what ſimple o2 vncompound numbers the number of the Solide may be reſolued into, and of the Characters, to thoſe Numbers ap-perteyning he ſhall be componed.

Example.

Of the firt Coſsicall number, 6 is componed of 2 and 3, 2 is the *Sq.* 3 the *Cu.* I conclude therfo2e the firt is a *S.Cube*, likewiſe of the eyght, 8 is made of 2, 2 and 2 therefo2e I in-ferre, that the eyght Character ſhal be a *S.S.Square.* Againe, 10 is made of 2, and 5 a *S S*, the tenth therefo2e ſhall be a *Sq.SSolide*, and thus of all other.

This I haue rather added for cuſtome ſake, bycauſe in all parts of the world theſe *Characters* and names of *Sq.* and *Cu.* &c.are vſed, but bycauſe I find another kinde of *Character* by my Father deuiſed, farre more readie in *Multiplications*, *Diuiſions*,and other *Coſsicall* operations,I will not doubt, ha-uing Reaſon on my ſide, to diſſent from common cuſtome

In this poynt, and vse these *Characters* ensuing:

① ② ③ ④ ⑤ ⑥ ⑦ ⑧ ⑨.

① for a *Roote*, ② for a *Square*, ③ for a *Cube*, ④ for a *Squared Square*, ⑤ for a *S. Solide*, ⑥ for a *Squared Cu.* and so of the rest, vsing only the ordinarie *Figures*, but somewhat turned a contrarie way, bycause they should be discerned, and not confused among others, and these shall be named *Primes*, *Seconds*, *Thirds*, *Fourths &c.* according to their *Figure* or *Character*.

Of Addition of Numbers Cosicall.

Chapter. 2.

When Numbers Cosicall are presented to be added, eyther it is of one or of mo, of one thus. I would adde 5 ① to 20 ① in this case the Characters being like, you shall only adde ẏ Numbers adioyning to the Character, so find yée that those two Cosicall numbers ioyned, make 25 ① but if the Characters be differente, as 10 ② to be added to 16 ③, then shall you ioyne them with this signe + Plus, saying they make added 10 ② + 16 ③, that is to saye 10 secondes more 16 thirds: for being of different Characters, they cannot be otherwise expressed, but if they be many to be added togither, then shall you dispose them one vnder another, matching always like Characters togither. For Example, I would adde 20 ① + 30 ② + 25 ④ vnto 45 ① + 16 ② + 13 ③.

In Addition of these kind of numbers, I begin from the left hand, saying 20 and 45 make 65, whereto I adioyne their common Character ①. Likewise 30 and 16 make 46, I adioyne ② their common Character.

20 ①	+	30 ②	+	25 ④		
45 ①	+	16 ②	+			13 ③
65 ①	+	46 ②	+	25 ④	+	13 ③

And bycause these nũbers are both noted with this signe +, I adde also that Signe. Last of all, bycause 25 and 13 doe differ in Character, I may not adde their numbers, as in the other, but put them downe with the signe + as in the Example you may behold.

Againe, it happeneth sometime, that albeit the Chara-ecters agrée, yet the Signes differ, as in this second Example.

$$10 \ /\!\!/ + 25 \ /\!\!/\!\!/ - 12 \ \chi$$
$$13 \ /\!\!/ - 22 \ /\!\!/\!\!/ + 16 \ \chi$$
$$23 \ /\!\!/ + 3 \ /\!\!/\!\!/ + 4 \ \chi$$

Here first 10 / and 13 / make 23 /, but bycause in the next the Signes are differente, I must deduct the lesse from the bigger, so remayneth 3, to the whiche I adde + viz. the Signe of the greater number. Againe, the next hauing diffe-rent Signes, I subtract the lesse out of the greater, there re-mayneth 4 χ whereto I annex + béeing the Signe of the greater. And thus the Addition appeareth to be 23 Primes + 3 feconds + 4 χ. Here is all the difficultie in this kind to vfe Subtraction, when the Signes differ, and fet downe the Signe of the greater, the whiche in one ſhorte sentence is ex-preſſed by Styfelius.

Diuerſa Signa commutant ſpeciem, A ponit M.

One Example more I thinke good to adioyne, to remoue all ſcruple or doubt that may ariſe. Theſe Operations con-ferred with the Rules of Addition enſuing, are manifeſt, and néede no farther Explanation.

$$4 \ \partial + 25 \ /\!\!/\!\!/ - 13 \ /\!\!/$$
$$6 \ \chi - 20 \ /\!\!/\!\!/ + 12 \ \chi$$
$$4 \ \partial + 6 \ \chi + 5 \ /\!\!/\!\!/ + 12 \ \chi - 13 \ /\!\!/$$

The rules of Addition.

If the Signes be like ſubſcribe the ſame Signe.
If vnlike Subtract, and to the Remaine adioyne the grea-ter Numbers Signe.

Of

Of Subtraction. Chap.3.

He like different difficulties are also in Subtraction, but
by one example contayning euerye particular varietie
that can chaunce, I thinke better briefely to teache, than by
vsing many wordes in euident matters to be tedious.

The rules of Subtraction.

Yke Signes produce their like, except the greater nūber
be from the leſſe to be ſubtract, then change the Signe &
ſet downe thereto the Difference.

Contrarie *Signes* in ſteade of *Subtraction*, requireth *Addition*, and to the *Product* adde the vpper numbers *Signe*.

8 ↄ + 12 ↄↄ	8 ↄ — 2 ↄↄ	— 7 ↄ + 10 ↄↄ
4 ↄ + 10 ↄↄ	2 ↄ + 2 ↄↄ	+ 5 ↄ + 12 ↄↄ
4 ↄ + 2 ↄↄ	6 ↄ — 4 ↄↄ	— 12 ↄ — 2 ↄↄ

Behold in theſe three Examples ye haue as many varieties as in Subtraction can happen, wherein this is to
be noted, that howſoeuer the nūbers are deliuered, ye may
alter and tranſpoſe them, ſo as like Characters be matched togither, alwayes keeping with them their conuenient
Signes, and placing alwayes the number to be Subtracted
vnder, and the other aboue. In the firſt Example we ſee the
Signes alike, deduct therefore one from the other, there remayneth firſt + 4 ↄ and in the ſeconde + 2 ↄↄ. But in
ye ſecond part of the ſecōd Example, the Signes are differēt
In ſteade therefore of Subtracting I adde, ſo amounteth
4 ↄↄ whereto I adioyne the Signe — bycauſe it is the vpper
numbers Signe. Againe in the third, bycauſe the Signes are
diuerſe in the firſt part by Addition I finde — 12 ↄ. But in
the ſeconde part albeit the Signes be one yet the greater nūber beyng vnder, I adioyne a contrarye Signe to the difference, ſaying the remayne is — 2 ↄↄ. And thus of al others.

Of Multiplycation. Chap. 4.

Oꝛ Multiplycation of Cossike numbers ye shall ad togither their Charecters, and the resulting Character, set downe with the number pꝛoduced of their numbers Multiplycation, and foꝛ the Signes these Rules ensuing must be obserued.

The same or like Signes multiplied produce + *Plus*.
Contrarie or diuerse Signes produce alway — *Minus*.

Euery seuerall number of the Multiplyer must be augmented in euerye number of the number to be multiplyed, and the Pꝛoductes with their coꝛrespondent Signes and Characters so placed, that like Characters be matched, and finally by Addition the whole collected.

Beholde the Example.

Firste I say 6 times 4 makes 24 and *Primes* added to Thirdes make Fourthes. I set downe therefoꝛe 24 ℞. Againe 6 times 12 make 72 and *Primes* added to Secondes, make ℥ I sette downe therefoꝛe 72 Thirdes, and in both these numbers the Signes being like, I sette downe +

$$4\,℥ + 12\,℔ - 4\,℔$$
$$6\,℔ + 1x\,℥ - 3\,℞$$
$$+48\,℞ + 24\,℞ + 72\,℥ - 24\,℔ + 144\,X - 12\,℔$$
$$-36\,℞ - 48\,℞ \qquad\qquad +12\,X$$
$$\overline{24\,℞ - 24\,℞ + 72\,℥ - 24\,℔ + 156\,X - 12\,℔}$$

Agayn 6 ℔ in 4 ℔ make 24 ℔, but bycause the Signes are different I adde to those 24 ℔ the Signe.—. This done, I dash 6 with the penne, and goe to the next Section oꝛ member of my Multiplyer *Viz*. 12 ℥ saying 12 ℥ in 4 ℥ Pꝛoduce 48 Sixs, I set downe therefoꝛe + 48 ℞. Againe 12 ℥
in

in 12 ꝑ pzoduceth 144 ✗ the Signes being like I adioyne +
Againe 12 ꝗ in 4 ꝶ maketh 48 ⅄ and the Signes beyng
vnlike I set downe —. This 48 ⅄ I set directlye vnder 24
⅄ in the vpper lyne . Againe dashing out 12 ꝗ I say 3 ⅄
in 4 ꝗ makes 12 ꝷ the which sette in the vpmost line by
cause there is none his like to set him vnder.

Again 3 ⅄ in 12 ꝶ maketh 36 ⅄ which I subscribe vn
der the Sixtes in the vpper line adding the Signe — bycause
the Signes are diuerse.

Finally 3 ⅄ in 4 ꝶ make 12 ✗ the which I sette vnder
the Fiftes in the firste row, adioyning the Signe +, bycause
both their Signes be like. And so drawing a lyne by Addi
tion, I finde the Product of that multiplication 24 ⅄ + 156
✗ + 72 ꝗ — 24 ⅄ — 24 ꝶ — 12 ꝷ. In like sort of al other,
for no other change can happen that you are not instructed
in by this Example.

Of Diuision. Chap. 5.

THe Diuision of numbers Cossical is not vnlike to the
Diuision of common numbers in respect of placing
the Diuisor; and as in Multiplycation the name to the
Character resulting was giuen by adding togither the two
Characters of the multiplyer and multiplyed number, so
here the Character of the Quotient is founde Subtracting
the Character of the Diuisor from the Character of the Di
uidende, as by the Example ensuing more plainely appea
reth: the Rule of the Signes is al one in Diuision with those
of Multiplycation.

Like

Like Signes giue +, Vnlike —.

The Number diuisible. 60 χ + 72 ℈ — 80 ♋ — 95 ℔ |6 ℔ — 8 ℔ *Quotient.*
The Diuisor. ℔ ℈ + ℔ ℔ 10 ℈ + 12 ℔
60 χ + 72 ℈

The Numbers thus digested, I search how oft 10 in 60, I finde 6 which I put in the Quotient adding this Charancter Seconds, bycause Thirdes from Fiftes leaue Seconds, that Quotient multiplyed in my whole Diuisor, maketh 60 χ + 7 2 ℈ which Deducted from the Diuisible, leaueth ∗ I remoue my Diuisor to the next, searching again how oft 10 in 80 I fynde 8, the whiche I put in the Quotient with hys Charecter ℔ bycause 3 from 4 leaues 1. And for as much as the Charecters are vnlike I set downe — multiply therefore — 8 ℔ in that Diuisor, there resulteth 80 ♋ — 96 ℔ the which Deducted from the Diuisible leaueth nothing, I conclude therefore 6 ℔ — 8 ℔ my Quotient. The which I may proue whether it be true two wayes, eyther multiplying the Diuisor with this Quotient so shall you produce the Diuisible number. Or diuiding the same Diuisible by youre Quotient so shal your first Diuisor in the newe Quotient be created.

Example.

60 χ — 80 ♋ + 72 ℈ — 96 ℔ |10 ℈ + 12 ℔
6 ℔ — 8 ℔ 6 ℔ — 8 ℔

I Fynde 6 in 60 contayned iust 10 times. Put 10 in the Quotient with the Character ℈ bycause 2 out of 5 leaueth 3. Nowe 10 ℈ multiplyed in the Diuisor maketh 60 χ — 80 ♋ which Deducted from the correspending parte of the Diuisible leaueth o. The Diuisor remoued I searche againe howe ofte 6 in 72, I finde iuste 12, that I put in the Quotient with the Character ℔ Primes, bycause 2 from 3 leaueth 1, and the Signes being like, I adde + thys 12 multiplyed

plyed in 6 ᴢ $- 8$ ℳ createth 72 ᴢ $- 96$ ℳ whiche deducted from the seconde parte of the Diuisible number, leaueth o. Thus haue ye in the Quotient broughte forthe your first Diuisor, & therfore are assured, both your works agræing, if you haue not erred. But if it happen that eyther the Characters agrée not, or the Signes and numbers so repugne as yée can not vse this ordinarie course of Diuision, then place them as a Fraction, drawing a line, and setting the Diuisible aboue, & the Diuisor vnderneath. These kind of Cossical Fractions haue their peculiar Rules, which shal hereafter ensue briefly, and so to Æquation.

Of Fractions Cossical. Chap. 6.

THe selfe same Rules that were taught for Addition, Subtraction, Multiplycation, and Diuision of common Fractions, serue also in these Cossical Fragments, as by these Examples ensuing shal appeare.

Examples of Addition.

The numbers Added.

$$\frac{36 ᴢ + 16 ℀}{12 \chi} , \quad \frac{9 ℳ + 4 ᴢ}{3 ᴢ} \quad Added \atop to \quad \frac{6 ᴢ - 2 ℳ}{4 ᴢ} \quad \Big| \quad \frac{18 \chi - 9 ℀}{12 \chi}$$

The Product. $\dfrac{18 \chi + 36 ᴢ + 7 ℀}{12 \chi}$

MVltiply the Denominators, so haue ye 12χ the cōmon Denominator, then crosse Multiplycation of $4 ᴢ$ in $9 ℳ + 4 ᴢ$ makes $36 ᴢ + 16 ℀$, and $3 ᴢ$ in $6 ᴢ - 3 ℳ$ makes $18 \chi - 9 ℀$. These added make this Fraction.

$$\frac{18 \chi + 36 ᴢ + 7 ℀}{12 \chi}$$

C.   Examples

Examples of Subtraction.

The Fraction
subduced.

$$\frac{16\mathfrak{q}+24\cancel{8}}{32\chi}\Bigg|\frac{4\mathcal{H}+6\mathcal{H}}{8\mathfrak{q}} \text{ } \substack{\textit{Deducted}\\ \textit{from}} \frac{3\mathcal{H}-2\mathcal{H}}{4\mathcal{H}}\Bigg|\frac{24\chi-16\cancel{8}}{32\chi}$$

$$\frac{24\chi-16\mathfrak{q}-40\cancel{8}}{32\chi}. \textit{ The Remayne.}$$

Examples of Multiplication.

$$\frac{6\mathcal{H}+3\mathfrak{q}}{4} \textit{ Multiplyed by } \frac{10\cancel{8}}{8\mathcal{H}} \textit{ Produceth } \frac{60\cancel{8}+30\mathcal{U}}{32\mathcal{H}}$$

$$\frac{5\mathcal{H}+32\mathfrak{q}}{7\mathfrak{q}-20\mathcal{H}} \textit{ Mul. } \frac{8\mathfrak{q}+10\mathcal{H}}{6\mathcal{H}-28\mathfrak{q}} \substack{\textit{Produ-}\\ \textit{ceth.}} \frac{256\cancel{8}+360\chi+50\cancel{8}}{602\cancel{8}-196\cancel{8}-120\mathcal{U}}$$

Examples of Diuision.

$$\textit{By } \frac{4\mathcal{H}}{3} \textit{ I wold diuide } \frac{16\chi+15\mathcal{H}}{9\mathcal{H}} \substack{\textit{ariseth of that}\\ \textit{Diuision}} \frac{+8\chi+45\mathcal{H}}{36\mathfrak{q}}$$

$$\textit{The Diui. } \frac{10\mathcal{H}}{16} \substack{\textit{The num. to}\\ \textit{be diuided.}} \frac{12\mathcal{H}+4}{12\mathcal{H}} \substack{\textit{The Quo-}\\ \textit{tient.}} \frac{192\mathcal{H}+64}{120\mathfrak{q}}$$

𝕿hese Examples are wrought euen in like sort & forme as the Fractions of Abstract Numbers, and their multiply= cation in respect of Signes and Characters, nothing differeth from that whiche alreadye hath bene declared in Integers Cossical.

FOr examination of al these kindes as wel Integers *Cossi-cal* as *Fragmēts*, this one Rule sufficeth. Admit any nūber what ye list for a *Roote* or *Prime*, and thereby set downe in Abstract numbers the value of euerye other *Cossical* nūber.
Then

Then with thofe *Abftract* numbers adde, *Subtract*, multiply or diuide, and conferre the *Productes* with *Coffical* numbers produced by thefe foretaught *Operatiõs:* If they agree, it fheweth a verity. If ye finde repugnaunce, Repetition in either kind difcouereth where the error refteth.

Of Reduction. Chap. 7.

REduction is two wayes vnderftand, eyther to Reduce a Fractiõ to his leaft Denomination, oz elfe to Reduce two Fractions of diuerfe Denominations to one & the fame Denomination.

The firft is perfozmed by diuiding both Numerator and Denominator by the greateft common Diuifor that may be founde.

The latter by croffe Multiplycation of the Numerator of one in the Denominator of the other, whereby refulteth ŷ new Numerators, and then multiplying the Denominators one in another, is Pzoduced the common Denominator.

Example.

I defire to reduce $\frac{16 \chi}{12 \chi}$ to a leffer Denomination, I diuide therefoze both Numerator and Denominator by 4 χ fo arifeth this Fraction $\frac{4 \text{\textit{H}}}{3}$ Equal to the fozmer Fraction. Oz if it happen that diuerfe Fractions be coupled togither by + oz — diuide euery member feuerallye by the greateft common Diuifor. Thus: $\frac{16 \chi}{12 \chi} + \frac{15 \text{\textit{H}}}{12 \chi}$ is Reduced to $\frac{4 \text{\textit{H}}}{3} +$ $\frac{5}{4 \text{\textit{H}}}$ diuiding the firft number of the Fraction by 4 χ and ŷ latter part by 3 χ. And thus of al fuch like.

THe latter kinde of Reduction by croffe Multiplycation is already fhewed in the Examples of Addition: but foz moze playneffe I wil giue one other Example.

E.ij.

12 ꝗ and 8 ✗ *Reduced to one Denomi-* } 48 ✗　24 ✗

3 ₦　　4 ѵ̷ *nation stande thus.* { 12 ꝗ　12 ꝗ

Ere 3 ₦ multiplyed in 4 ѵ̷ make 12 ꝗ the comon Denominator, and 12 ꝗ multiplyed crosse in 4 ѵ̷ maketh 48 ✗. Likewise 8 ✗ in 3 ₦ augmented, createth 24 ✗ so are the two proponed Fractions reduced $\frac{48\ ✗}{12\ ꝗ}$ being as much as $\frac{12\ ꝗ}{3\ ₦}$ and $\frac{24\ ✗}{12\ ꝗ}$ no lesse then $\frac{8\ ✗}{4\ ѵ̷}$ and betwæne themselues of equal Denomination. This Rule is vniuersall for al Fractions, of how manye Sections or members soeuer they consist. Now to *Æquations.*

Of Aequations.

AEquation is nothing else but a certain conference of two numbers being in value Equal, and yet in multitude and Denomination different.

As we maye say 1 Pounde is Equal to 20 shillings, or 3 Pounds equal to 12 Crownes, or 4 ѵ̷ is Equal to 8 ₦ or 3 ꝗ is Equal to 6 ѵ̷. In all these their value agrée, albeit the Numbers and Denominators or Characters be diuerse. Of these *Æquations* I will speake the more particularlye, for that all the Operations of *Algebra* tende to this finall ende, to frame an *Æquation,* and then thereby to search the Value of the Roote, or *Prime,* wherby the most difficult Questions that maye arise or be proponed, are wyth farre more facilitye to be resolued, than by anye other Rules whatsoeuer.

Of

Of Reduction of Æquations.

The Reduction which is sought in Æquatiō, is to bring one part of the Æquation, to one simple Cossicall number viz. 1 ℳ, 1 ℀, 1 ℥, or so forth, the whiche is done two wayes.

First, by transposing or remouing of numbers from one part, to the other.

Then by reducing those numbers so transposed, to theyr least Denomination, or if they be Fractions, to an Integer.

Of transporting of numbers in Æquations.

This is a Rule generall, euerie number transposed changeth his Signe, as if I say 10 ℳ +4 are Equall to 3 ℀, I may trāsferre 4 to 3 ℀, & say 10 ℳ are Equall to 3 ℀ — 4. Likewise, as 2 ℥ + 10 ℳ are equall to 3 ℀ — 6, so is 2 ℥ equall vnto 3 ℀ — 6 — 10 ℳ, and this for transporting of Signes sufficeth, whereby alway you may reduce one side of the Æquation, to one particular Cossicall Number.

This kinde of Reduction by transportation, must be so ordered, that you single by himselfe the greatest Character, so as the same may stande solitarie on the one side, and the lesser Characters frame the cōtrarie part of the Æquation.

Of Reduction of the parts of an Æqua-
tion, to their least *Denomination*.

One part of the Æquation being reduced by trāsportation of numbers, to one simp'e Cossicall Character, To reduce the Æquation to a lesser Denominatiō, you shal diuide eyther part by some common Diuisor, the greatest you can finde.

As if 3 ℀ be equall to 12 ℥ — 9 ℳ diuiding by 3 ℳ I finde 1 ℥ Equall to 4 ℳ — 3.

G.iij.   Sometime

Sometime it shall be requisite to take away some number from eyther part of the Æquation, as if I haue 6 ♯ Equall to 12 ♯ — 24, deducting from eyther part of the Æquation 6 ♯, there resteth ∅ Equall to 6 ♯ — 24, and therefore of necessitie 6 ♯ is equall to 24, for this Rule is generall. That if you bring an Æquation (by suche Deduction) to a ∅ on the one part, there must be some member in the other connexed with the Signe Minus, the whiche is alwayes Equall to all the rest of that part of the Æquation.

Sometimes Reduction is made by adding togither all suche parcels, as on the one side of the Æquation haue equal Characters, as if 1 ✕ be Equal to 3 ℥ + 16 ♯ — 1 ½ — 10 ♯. Here by adding + 16 ♯ to — 10 ♯, there resulteth + 6 ♯, so that I say 1 ✕ is equall to 3 ℥ + 6 ♯ — 1 ½, and ẙ same diuided by 1 ♯ maketh 1 ✕ Equal to 3 ½ + 6 — 1 ♯.

Reduction of Fragments vvhich shall
happen in Æquations to Integers.

Another kinde of Reduction there is of Fragmentes to whole numbers, whiche commeth in vse when an Æquation is founde betwéene Fractions on the one or both parts, as if

$$\frac{4\,½ + 2\,℥}{2\,♯} \text{ be Equall vnto } \frac{3\,℥ — 2\,½}{1\,♯}$$

by crosse multiplication of the Denominator of the one in the Numerator of the other, I finde these two numbers produced 4 ℥ + 2 ✕, and 6 ✕ — 4 ℥. Betwene these, the like Æquation remayneth, and the same first reduced by transporting of Signes, maketh 4 ℥ Equall to 6 ✕ — 2 ✕ — 4 ℥. Then by Addition of 6 ✕ to — 2 ✕, there resulteth 4 ✕ — 4 ℥, equall to 4 ℥. Againe, diuiding either part of the Æquation by 4 ½, there resulteth 1 ♯ Equall to 1 ½ — 1 ♯. And last of all, deducting 1 ♯ from both partes of the Æquation, I find ∅ equall to 1 ½ — 2 ♯, and therfore of necessity as was declared

declared before 1 ℔, Equall to 2 ℔. Thus of that intricate Fraction, you sée how we haue by the former Rules produced this playne and facile Æquation. These Examples well laboured,will make all Æquations familiar.

The demonſtration of all theſe rules, hang on the thirde common ſentence, and the fiftenth Propoſition of the fifth Booke of the Elements of Geometrie.

The Rule of Coſſ.or Algebra.
Chapter. 8.

THis Rule is of ſuche perfection, that it perfourmeth not onely whatſoeuer maye be done by the rule of *Proportion*,the rule of falſe *Poſitions*, the rule of *Allegation*, the Rules of *Archindus*,ſixe quantities of *Cataym*, or of any or all other *Rules* that euer haue bin inuented, but alſo with ſuch facilitie and ſenſible *Methode* proceedeth in all his operations, that it may well be accounted the *Prince* and *Gouerneſſe* of al other. Leauing therfore to waſt words in ſuch by branches, I will bring thee to the *Fountayne* head, whence all other *Rules*,as particular Chanels are deriued. The *Rule* enſueth.

The Rule.

FOr the number ſought, ſet downe 1 ℔, then proceede in youre Arithmeticall workings , according to the forme and nature of the queſtion,till you come to ſome Æquatiō,the which being reduced,as is before taught,you ſhall by the number of that parte of the Æquation,whyche conſiſteth of one ſole Coſſicall, diuide the other parte of the Æquation only,if youre ſole Character be ℔. Or from the ſame extract ſutch a Roote, as the Character of your ſolitarie ſide demonſtrateth. The firſt Quotient or Roote thereof,ſhall be the vnknowen or deſired Number.

Example.

Example.

This Rule can not be better explaned, than by example. Admitte therefore I am demaunded what number that should be, whose third and fourth partes ioyned, maketh 14. According to the rule I say, it is 1 ⅟ viz. one Prime, or one Roote, as commonlye Algebricians tearme it. Nowe the whole cunning resteth in discouering the value of this Prime or Roote.

I reason therefore thus, if the number I séeke bée one Prime, then is ⅓ and ¼ of a Prime added togither 14, but ⅓ ⅟, & ¼ ⅟ added, maketh $\frac{7}{12}$ ⅟ therfore is $\frac{7}{12}$ ⅟ equall to 14. Behold an Æquatiõ, the which bycause it is already simple and néede no Reduction, accor̛ding to this Rule with $\frac{7}{12}$ béing the number of my solitarie Character, I diuide 14, the other part of my Æquation. Of this Diuisiõ, resulteth 24. I conclude therefore 24 to be the number soughte, whose third and fourth parte added, shoulde make 14. In this Æquation, bycause the solitarie Character is ⅟, the quotient of the Diuision discouereth the number sought, but if the solitarie Character had bin ⅟, then shoulde you haue extracted from youre Quotient 14 his Quadrate Roote, if ꝫ the Cubike Roote.

Another Question.

THere is a bande of Souldyoures armed with three sortes of Weapon, Pikes, Halberdes, and Shot. The Halberdes and Shotte put togyther, are double so manye as the Pykes, and the Pykes and Shotte togyther, are eyght times so manie as the Halberds. And the Shot by themselues alone, are in number more than both the other weapons by 55. I demaund the number of Souldiers in that band, and the number of euerie sort of weapon.

For the number of the Halberdes, I put 1 ⅟, then must both the other weapons togither be 8 ⅟, being by Supposition 8 times so many, and the Pikemen 3 ⅟, for so dothe the

res〈t〉us

refiue(being 5 ⫟ for the Shotte, added to 1 ⫟ for the Halberds)become double to 3 ⫟ the Halberds by Suppofition. Now feeing in my queftiō it is fayd, that the Shot are more than both the reſt by 55, I adde 1 ⫟ my Halberds, to 3 ⫟ my Pikes, there arifeth 4 ⫟, whiche deducted from 5 ⫟, the Shot leaueth 1 ⫟ Equall to 55. Thus haue I an Æquation. Nowe diuiding 55 by 1, the number of the follitarie Character, there arifeth in the Quotient againe 55. I conclude therefore 1 ⫟ to be 55, and fo 55 Halberdiers in that band. When the Pikes being 3 ⫟, muft be 155, and the Shot being 5 ⫟ are 275. All thefe added togither, make 495, thus finde I fiue hundred Souldiers faue fiue to be in the whole Band. But bycaufe fuch Equations many times fhal happen, as the folitarie Signe fhall be a ⫟, I will in the next Chapter fhew how to extracte the Quadrate Roote of fundrie forts of Æquations.

Hovve to extraɥ the fecond Radix or
Quadrate roote of any *Coſſicall* numbers, a-
rifing in any Equations.
Chap. 9.

Forafmuch as alreadie in Reduɥion, I haue taught fo to order the Æquatiō, that the Charaɥers of the fecōd part of the Æquation fhall alway be leffe than the fingled Charaɥer. This is moſt certaine, that the extraɥion of the Second Roote, or fquare Radix of Coſſicall Numbers, is neuer in any Arithmeticall operation neceffarie, faue onely of thefe varieties following.

To finde the Quadrate or feconde Radix of

{
A Number alone
⫟ or Rootes onely.
⫟ + Numbers.
Numbers — ⫟.
⫟ — Numbers.
}

℞.

Thefe

These are the only fiue varieties, wherein the extraction of Rootes Quadrate in these Cossicall Æquations are requi= red, and for euerie of these briefe Rules shall ensue.

Rules.

1 For the firste, I referre you onely to the firſt Booke of my Fathers, where you are taught out of anye abſtracte or ſimple number or Fraction, to extract his Square *Radix*.

2 In the ſeconde, the number it ſelfe that is with the rootes coupled, is the number or *Radix* deſired.

3 In the third, you ſhall take the moytie of the number of ℋ or Rootes.

This moytie ſquare, adde the ſame to the Number Ab= ſtract in your Æquation.

To the Quadrate *Radix* of that Producte, adioyne the moytie firſt vſed.

The Number reſulting of this laſt Addition, is youre de= ſired *Radix*.

4 In the fourth, ſet downe (as before) the moytie of the ℋ number that *N*.Square. That Square adde to the number Abſtract, and from the roote Quadrate of the Product, de= duct the moytie firſt ſet downe. This Remayne is the deſi= red Roote.

5 In the fifth kind there is alway two Rootes, vnleſſe the moitie of the ℋ ſquared, be equall to the number Abſtract, for then is the moitie of the ℋ number the *Radix* ſoughte. But howſoeuer that fall out, you ſhall as before reſerue the moytie of the Primes, firſt ſquaring the ſame, and from that Square, deducting the Abſtract number. The Roote Qua= drate of the Remaynder, added to youre reſerued moytie, maketh the greater *Radix*, the ſame quadrate roote dedu= cted from the moytie reſerued, leaueth the leſſer Radix.

The firſt and ſecond of theſe Rules, being of themſelues manifeſt, néede no farther Explanation. Of the other thrée, particular Examples ſhall enſue.

Example

Example of the third Rule.

$$1 \; ∦ \; ℈ \; 6 \; ℥ + 27$$

Admitte this Æquation 1 ∦ ℈ 6 ℥ + 27. The Moytie of 6 is 3, that Squared, is 9, which added to 27, maketh 36, the Roote Square of that is 6, whereto adioyning 3, the Moytie first vsed, I make 9, the Radix of that Æquation.

Example of the fourth Rule.

$$1 \; ∦ \; ℈ \; 80 - 2 \; ℥$$

Héere you are to Extract the Square Roote of 80 lesse 2 Primes or Rootes. The moytie of 2 is 1, that Squared maketh 1, this added to the abstract number, maketh 81 hys Roote square is 9, from that I deduct 1 my firste moytie, so resteth 8, the Radix of that Equation.

Example of the fifth Rule.

$$1 \; ∦ \; ℈ \; 14 \; ℥ - 33$$

The Moytie of the number of Primes is 7, that squared, maketh 49, from this I deduct 33, the abstracte number, resteth 16, whose Roote 4 added to 7, the Moytie Fundamentall, maketh 11, the greater Roote, deduct the same 4 from 7, resteth 3 the lesser *Radix.* The truth whereof is thus apparant, square 11 ariseth 121, the Square which shoulde be equall to 14 Rootes lesse 33, 14 times 11 maketh 154 the number of the Rootes, from this deduct 33, the abstract number resteth 121 your Square. In like sort, the lesser Roote 3 squared, maketh 9. Now 14 of these Rootes are 42, from whiche deduct 33 resteth 9 the Square. And héereby it is manifest, that both the one and the other are true Rootes of this Æquation, and moe than these it is impossible to finde.

AMASIAS.

S *Tyfelius* for ayde of memorie in this one word *Amasias,* represēteth the rules of these 3 Æquatiōs, by *A* or *Ha,* we

H.ij.   may

may remember the firſte halfe or *Moytie*, the foundation of all the operations, and therefore may be tearmed the *Moitie Fundamental*. *M* ſignifyeth *Multiplication* of that moytie in it ſelfe, whiche I name *Squaring*. *A* and *S Additton* and *Subtraction*, *viz.* in the two former *Æquatiõs*, to adde the *Square* of the *Moitie* to the abſtract number, In the laſt to *Subtract* the one from the other, *I*, ſignifieth the *Inuentiõ* of the Square Roote of the *Product* or *Remayne*, then *A* and *S* agayne admoniſheth *Addition* or *Subtraction* of this *Roote* to be made too or from the *Moitie Fundamentall*, in forme as the *Signe* of that *Mottie* declareth.

Queſtions concerning the office of the Serieant Maior. Chap. 10.

The firſt Queſtion.

Here is deliuered to the Serieant Maior 60 Enſignes, in euerie Enſigne 160 Pikes, and ſhort weapon. The Generals pleaſure is, that he ſhall put them into one mayne Squadrone, and to arme it rounde with ſeauen ranckes of Pikes, I demaund how many Pikes, how many Halberds, he ſhall vſe to make the greateſt Squadrone, and howe manye Ranckes ſhall be in that Battayle.

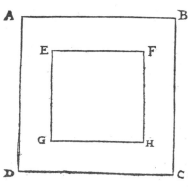

For reſolution of this demaund, Firſt I ſet downe in Portrayte the forme of the Battayle here repreſented, by A B C D. The Squadrone of ſhort weapon E F G H. The reſidue repreſenting the ſeauen Ranckes of the Armed Pikes. Seeing therefore I haue 60 Enſignes, and in euerie Enſigne 160 of Pikes & ſhort weapon.

I multiply 160 by 60, resulteth 9600 the number of men deliuered to be Embattelled. Now since I am demaunded the number of eyther weapon, and also the number of Ranckes represented by the lyne A D o2 A B, I saye that is 1 ℀ according to the Rule of Cosse. This multiplyed in it self, maketh 1 ℀ the Square A B C D, the whiche is E-qual to 9600 the number of men to be imbattelled. Thus am I come to this Equation 1 ℀ ℀ to 9600. The greatest Roote of Integers is 97, the lyne A D o2 A B Viz. the number of Rankes,

Now consideryng E F the side of the Squadron of shorte weapon is 1 4 lesse: (being armed round which 7 Rankes of Pikes.) I Deduct 14 out of 97, remayneth 83 the side E F, whose Square is 6889 the number of the Short weapō, and that Deducted from 9409, the Square of 97, leaueth 2520 the number of Pikes. Thus I finde a Resolution of the demaundes as followeth.

The Number of Pykes. } 2520 The number of Shorte weapon. } 6889 Rankes in all. } 97 Rankes of Short weapon. } 83

The second Question.

THe high *Marshal* commaundeth that the Army shall be diuided into 3 like square Battels, euery Battayle to bee Aimed in the fronte with 7 Rankes of Pikes, and that these battels making one fronte vppon the Enimie be em-paled on eyther side with a sleeue of Pikes of 5 in a ranke. This order being prescribed, he deliuereth the *Serieāt Maior*, 18000 *Souldiours* pikes and short weapō, commaunding that the *Squadrons* be made as greate as possible may be of those men. It is demaunded how manye in euerye ranke of the *Battallions*, and in what sort the *Serieant Maior* shal shift his weapons: howe many pikes for the sleeues, and howe

H.iiij.   many

many of ſhort weapons and pikes in euerye Battallion ſeuerally.

To reſolue this Queſtion, firſt I put the Marſhals oꝛder
in Figure, A B C repꝛeſenting the 3 Battels armed in the
fronte with 7 ranckes of Pikes: D and E the Sleeues 5 in a
Ranke.

G

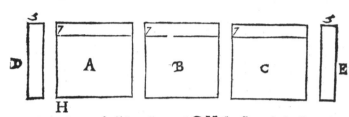

H

Now bycauſe I knowe not G H the ſiꝛe of the Battel oꝛ
length of the ſlæues I ſuppoſe that 1 ⅟₁, the which increſed
by 5 maketh 5 ⅟₁ foꝛ one ſlæue, that doubled maketh 10 ⅟₁
foꝛ the 2 ſlæues, then Square 1 ⅟₁ ſo haue I 1 ⅟₁ the quantitie of one Battel, and ſo conſequentlye 3 ⅟₁ foꝛ the 3 Battels. Which adioyned to 10 ⅟₁ ẏ 2 ſlæues maketh 3 ⅟₁ + 10
⅟₁ foꝛ Battels and ſlæues. But that ſhould be 18000, foꝛ ſo
many mē were deliuered to make ẏ Battels. Behold therefoꝛe the Equation 3 ⅟₁ + 10 ⅟₁ ❌ 18000, which reduced maketh 1 ⅟₁ + ¹⁰⁄₃ ⅟₁ ❌ 6000 and ſo conſequentlye 1 ⅟₁ ❌ 6000
— ¹⁰⁄₃ ⅟₁. The Value of this Roote by ẏ fourth Rule is fou̅d
to be 75 and certain Fractions which always in theſe _Mi-_
litare Queſtions may be omitted. I conclude therefoꝛe euerẏ
Battel muſt haue 75 in a Ranke, and that multiplyed by 5
maketh 375 the number of Pikes in eyther ſlæue. And bycauſe the Battels are armed in the fronte with 7 Rankes
of Pikes, I multiply 7 in 75, ſo haue I 525, the number of
Pikes in euerẏ Squadron, and that Deducted from 5625
the Square of 75, reſteth 5100 the number of ſhoꝛt weapon
in euerẏ Squadron. Thus ſtandeth euerẏ demaunde reſolued as followeth.

Pykes

Pykes in eyther Sleeue.	} 375.	Pykes in euery Squadron.	} 525.	Short weapon in euery Squadron	} 5625.

The number of Ranckes in euery Squadron.	} 75.

The thirde Queſtion.

THere is deliuered to the *Serieaunt Maior* 8500 *Soldiours* with commaundemente that he embattel them in ſuche ſort that euery *Souldiour* in front ſtande three foote diſtant from other, and euery Ranke from other 7 foote, obſeruing this Ordinaunce he is commaunded to frame of theſe men the greateſt Battayle that maye bee to make the grounde ſquare. I demaunde howe many in a Ranke, and how many Rankes in that battayle.

For the number of Rankes I ſuppoſe 1 ⅟ then muſt the number of Souldiours in a Rancke be ⅞ ⅟ theſe multiplyed togither make ⅞ ⅟ Equal to 8500 the whole nūber, whych Equation reduced ſtandeth thus, 1 ⅟ ℈ 3643 ⅓ and ſo by the firſt Rule of Æquations. I finde the Roote 60 with a Fraction whiche here neglected I affirme 60 Rankes in that Battayle, which multiplyed by 7 and diuided by 3 maketh 140 the number of Souldiours in euery Ranke.

The number of Rankes.	} 60	The number of Souldiours in euery Ranke.	} 140.

HOw by this Art of *Algebra* or Rule of Coſſe as the *Italians* terme it. The *Serieant Maior* or *Serieant General* may readily imbattel his *Souldiours* in what order ſoeuer it ſhal pleaſe the General or high Marſhal to commaunde.

Infinite

*I*Nfinite *are the Formes of imbattelling, some* Circular *as appea-reth by* Iulius Cæfar *in his* Commentaries *when he declareth how his Armie* Globo Facto, *defended themselues, some* Triangular, *as in the same* Commentaries *maye be seene where his* Souldiours *being inuironed of their Enimies* Cuneo facto eru-pére : *Some raunged in forme of* Lunula, *wherein the* Turke *e-spec₊allie delyteth , reposing a certaine superstitious confidence in the Figure. But whosoeuer shal wel consider how impossible it is for any of these or like formes to* Martch *and maintayn their aray, as* Souldiours *in our age are trayned , shal be compelled to confesse the* Squadron *and* Battels *made and framed of* Squadrons *only in these our warres able to be vsed. And no doubt if the* Turkishe Ariny *martch and maintayne that forme, it must be by diuiding the same into many* Squadrons, *placing them in suche* Lunular *forme,& then euery of those* Squadrons *by the directiõ of discreet* Colonels *martching vnited, mãy maintayne their aray,& stil re-present that their* Lunular Figure. *The like I suppose of the* Romanes *whose* Legions *were altogither componed of* Square Cohorts. *Seing therfore the best & surest, or rather the only kinds of* Embattelling *as wel to* Martch *as to* Fight , *is* Square *or componed of* Squares , *It shal be only needeful for the* Serieant General *to set downe in* Figure *the maner of embattelling by the* General *commaunded, as I haue in the former questions alreadye shewed, and then accordingly to proceed in his* Operations, *allowing for euery* Squadron 1 *ι/ι & for euery number of* Souldiours *aunswering to the side of a* Battalion *in impalement or other-wise, only allowing* 1 *ι/ι so proceeding til he come to the* Equation.

Finally, *by the Art before taught searching out the* Value *or number of the ι/ι and ι/ι, he hath the number of* Souldiours *in e-uery* Battallion, *and the number of* Souldiours *in euery* Ranke, *togither with the numbers of* Souldiours *and* Rankes *in euerye impalemente, wings &c. as by the former questions and their ope-rations maye euidently appeare. And by this Art the* Serieaunte General *shal be able suddainely, how great soeuer the multitude be, to change their forme of embattelling into as manye sundrye or-*

ders

ders as he shal bee enioyned, or in respecte of the Enimy, or the place shal be founde conuenient.

Certaine Questions touching the Office of the high Marshall and Campe
Maister. Chap.11.

ALthough the forme of *Camps* may be altered according to the diuersitie of *Situations*, in respecte of Riuers, or woods that do adioyne therto, yet for lodging both *Horseme* and *Footemen* commodiously readily and without confusiõ, there is none better than the *Square*. It behoueth therefore those Officers to vnderstand first what quantitie of ground sufficeth for the lodging and encamping of some certayne *Regiment* of *Horsemen* and *Footemen*, which knowen, by the *Rules* ensuing, he shal be able to extende the same to al nũ-bers, and to knowe readily vpon the viewe of any grounde what number it is able to receyue both of *Footemen* and Horse, and accordingly to giue order to inferiour *Officers* in what sorte they shall proceede to diuide their grounde for euery *Regiment*.

The firste Question.

ADmit I finde by experience that 3000 footemen maye commodiously be encamped in a plat of grounde 300 pace *Square*. I demaunde how many pace the ground shold be square that shall receyue 1000. Footemen.

To resolue this Question, I say the number of pace de-maunded is 1 ⁴⁄₄ the *Square* therof is 1 ⅛ of paces, the whi-che is able to receyue the 10000. then saye I thus by the Rule of Proportion 10000 giueth 1 ⅛ of paces, what yel-deth 3000, by Multiplycation and Diuision, I finde the fourth Proportional number $\frac{3}{10}$ ł wherby it appereth, that in the Campe of 3000 there is $\frac{3}{10}$ ł of paces, but in that Campe by suppoſition there is 90000 paces, foz ſo much is 300 multiplyed in it ſelfe. Beholde therefoze your Equation.

$$\frac{3}{10} \text{ ł} \mathfrak{X} 90000 \; Paces.$$

The Value of the Roote founde by the firſte Rule of E-quations is betwæene 549 an 550: ſo manye paces therefoze oughte the grounde to be Square that ſhal receyue 10000 men.

The Second Queſtion.

I Finde by experience that 1000 *Horſemen* will demaunde as much grounde to encampe on as 10000 *Footemen*, I find alſo by experience that 550 pace Square of grounde wyll ſuffice to receyue eyther of them in one maine Squadron *Campe*, but my deſire is to diuide eyther of them into 3 *Regiments*, and to lodge them ſeuerally in 3 ſquare *Campes*. I demaunde how many pace Square euery of thoſe *Campes* muſt bee.

Foz the number ſoughte I ſet downe 1 ł that Square maketh 1 ł of paces, the Superficial content of one of the 3 Camps. Therefoze ſhall the thzée Campes be 3 ł of paces, but thoſe thzée were contayned in 302500 paces, foz ſo muche is the contente Superficiall of the Campe of 550 pace Square. Beholde therefoze your Equation.

The Æquation.

3 ł $\mathfrak{X}$ 302500 { *which reduced makes* } 1 ł $\mathfrak{X}$ 100833 $\frac{1}{3}$ *paces.*

The value of the *Prime* ſearched as befoze is taught, is 317 pace, and ſo much Square ought euery one of the thzée Foote Campes and Horſe Camps to bée, foz the conuenient receite of ſuch Regiments.

The

The thirde Queſtion.

EXperience teacheth, that to encampe 6000 Footemen and 600 Horſe, in ſuch commodious maner that all the ſtreetes maye bee of reaſonable breadth, the Market place and place of aſſembly of ſufficient Capacitie, Rome ſufficient for the Munition, with a Ring and trenche meete to receyue the *Sentinels* and Souldiours for defence, togither with the Carriages to impale the ſame Campe . To performe theſe dueties commodiouſly, it is requiſite the Camp ſhoulde be 32 ſcore pace Square. But there is deliuered by the Generall 30000 footemen, and 3000 Horſe: I demaund what ſcope of grounde the Lord high Marſhall or Campe Maiſter ſhould appoynt to receyue this company lodging them as commodiouſly as the other.

For the number of ſcore or paces in the ſide of this new Campe whoſe quantitie is deſired accoꝛding to the Rule of Coſſe, I ſette doune 1 ℔ and bycauſe the Horſemen and Footemen, in eyther Campe are pꝛopoꝛtionally ſoꝛted , I adioyn the numbers of Horſemen and Footemen togither, which make 33000 and ſeeing the ſide of this new Campe is 1 ℔ of paces, the Superficial Capacitie muſt be 1 ℔ of paces. I ſay therfoꝛe if 33000 Souldiours, require 1 ℔ paces to encampe, what ſhal 6600 the number of Souldiours in the leſſe Campe : There ariſeth ⅕ ℔ paces, but by Suppoſition that little Campe contayned 409600 paces, foꝛ ſo manye are in 32 ſcore Square.

Beholde therefore the *Æquation*.

The Equation.

| ⅕ ℔ Ӿ 409600 *paces* | { This Reduced maketh } | 1 ℔ Ӿ 2048000 *paces*. |

I.V.   Ans

And so the value of the *Prime* by *Extraction* of the Roote as is taughte in the Chapter of Æquations falleth out betwéene 1431 and 1432 paces. So is the side of the newe Campe. 71 score 12 paces.

But if the Horsemen and Footemen had not bene Proportionally forted to the numbers in youre Little Campe: then is the readiest and surest way seuerally, by the Arte shewed in the first and second Question, to cast howe much grounde eyther Horse Campe and Foote Campe wil require, allowing conuenient groundplats for Market place, & places of assembly, with Streets to part the sayd Campes, and also space sufficient for the Ring of the Campe, proportionally, according to the increase of the numbers of Souldiours to be encamped. Finally adding togyther the superficial contente of those Campes , places of assemblye, and stréetes &c. There resulteth the superficiall quantitie of the whole Campe, which reduced into paces, the Roote Quadrate thereof is the number of paces contayned in the side of that Campe . And hereof I néede adioyne no Example, considering there is nothing else in this Operation but a reiteration of the former workings seuerallye for eyther Campe, the places of assemblye, the stréets, &c. trasferring by the Rule of Proportion the measures from one Campe proportinally to another.

The fourth Question.

HOw the highe Marshal or Campe maister whatsoeuer number of Horsemen and Footemen shal be deliuered vnto him, may redily coniecture what quantitie of ground wil suffice strongly and commodiously to encampe them, and howe muche he oughte to allowe to eyther Horsecampe or foote Campe seuerally.

To

To refolue this Queſtion, it is cōuenient to know what quantitie of grounde is to be allowed to a Horſeman, and how much to a Footeman, and this is only by experience to be learned, and among the experimented Souldyoures of diuers ages and Nations, I finde diuerſitie of Opinions. Monſieur Lange alloweth to euery Footeman 90 Quadrate foote of earth, and to euery man of Armes 900, and to euerie Eſtradiote and light Horſeman 800. Others following the Romanes, aſſigne to euerie Footeman a Quadrate platte of ground ſixe foote bꝛoade, and tenne foote long, and to euerie Horſeman one with an other the lodging of thꝛeé footemen. The Romanes ſought alwayes to encampe ſtrongly, preſſing nigh togither, not regarding pleaſure oꝛ commoditie. But as their Proportion is ſomewhat tw ſtreight foꝛ Souldiorie trayned in this our age, whiche can neyther away with the anoyances, ne yet with the hard dyet, which was familiar to the Romanes: ſo iudge I the foꝛmer Proportion of Monſieur Lange, ouermuche to dilate and enlarge the Camp, and therefoꝛe conſidering the ſtreétes that diuide the Hoꝛſe and foote Campe, muſt be large, and alſo betweéne euerie Regiment in eyther Camp, there muſt be conuenient wayes and paſſages, neyther by ouermuche delating the Campe to make it weake, ne yet by ouer ſtreightning of the Lodgings and paſſadges, to peſter the Souldiorie, I hold it conuenient to allow to euerie Footeman, 80 ſquare foote of earth, and to euerie Horſeman 400, and foꝛ the places of Aſſemblie, the Market place, the Butcherie, the Victuallers, and place to receyue the Munition and Ordinance, with the Pioners, and other Mechanicall artificers as much moꝛe as both Campes amount vnto, ſo will there fall out after the Ring of the Campe is deſcribed of conueniente largeneſſe, and all ſtreétes and paſſages in pꝛopoꝛtion anſwerable with due place to receyue the Colonels, Captaynes, and Officers of euerie Bande particularly, that then the Loꝛgings of a Footeman ſhall not amount vnto aboue 50

fœte, and euerie Horſeman one with another 250. To reſolue therefore this Queſtion, you ſhall multiplie ẙ number
of fœtemen by 80, for the ſuperficiall content of the Foote-
camp, and the number of Horſemen by 400 for the Horſe-
camp, the Products adde togyther, and double the reſulting
ſumme. The Roote Quadrate of this laſt produced number diuided by 3, deliuereth in the Quotient howe manye
Paſe ſquare the Campe ſhall be, whiche may both ſtrongly
and commodiouſlie lodge youre propoſed Armie. And the
Rootes Quadrate of the contentes ſuperficiall of eyther
Camp diuided by 3, doth alſo deliuer howe many Paſe the
ſide of eyther Camp ſhall be.

Example.

Admitte I haue 30000 Footemen, and 6000 Horſe to
bée encamped, I multiplie 30000 by 80, ariſeth 2400000.
I augmente alſo 6000 by 400, ariſeth likewiſe 2400000,
theſe ioyned, make 4800000, whyche doubled, preſenteth
9600000, the Quadrate Roote héereof is 3093, whiche parted by 3, bringeth in the Quotiente 1031. So manye paſe
ſhall the ſide of that Square Campe bée, whyche ſhall
lodge the thirtie thouſande fœtemen, and ſixe thouſande
Horſe. If the Enimie be at hande, I would haue alwayes
the Ring and Trench of the Campe within, but if the Enimie be not doubted, they may be made withoute this proportion of Camp, whereby the ſtréetes and lodgings maye
be enlarged.

The more ample handling of this office,
referred to another Treatiſe.

I Mighte heere adioyne ſundrye formes and orders of
Encamping, vſed by ſundrye Nations, and therevppon
frame a greate number of *Arithmeticall Queſtions*, but I
reſerue the more ample handling of thys matter, to another

ther Treatife of *Fortification* of Townes and Campes,
wherein I will declare howe by the *Topographicall Instru-
mente* defcribed in my *Pantometria*, the high Marfhall fud-
daynelie maye fette downe the *Ring* of the *Campe*, that
fhall receyue anye Armie that fhall by the *Generall* bee
committed vnto hym, afsigning to euerie Regimente hys
Quarter, and howe wyth lyke celeritie the *Campe Mayster*
or *Prouostes* of euerie Regimente fhall diftribute theyr
Bandes, and the *Harbinger* of euerie Bande hys feuerall
Lodgings, fo that the Armie fhall fpeedily, ftrongly, and
commodiouflie be lodged, withoute confufion or diforder.
And for thys prefente Treatife, beyng onely *Arithmeti-
eall*, thefe fewe Queftions maye fuffice to gyue fome lyght
to the *Ingenious Souldyoure*, to fearche farther how thys *Arte*
maye ftande hym in ftead, for exact readie difpatch in hys
Militarie Actions.

Certayne Queftions Arithmeticall,
concerning the office of the Mayfter
of the Ordinance.

Chap. 1 2.

IF a Falcon of three ynches Bullet wey 500 Pounde, I
demaunde howe muche a Cannon of eyght ynches wyll
weygh, that is able to receyue hys proportionall charge to
that Falcon.

This Queftion by the fimple Rule of Proportion, can
not be anfwered, for as mutch as weight is peculiarly ap-
perteyning neyther to lines nor Superficies, but onely vnto
Solide bodyes. Seing therefore as it is by Euclid demon-
ftrate, and in my Pantometria I haue alreadie taught, that
Spheres, and al other like and vniforme bodies, be in Triple
the proportion of their Diameters, you fhall multiplie either
Diame-

Diameter o2 heyght of the Bullets Cubically, and wyth those Cubicall numbers, wo2ke acco2ding to the rule of Proportion, as by the Example enſuing mo2e playnely ſhall appeare.

Example.

The Cube of 3 is 27, the Cube of 8 is 512. Nowe by the Rule of p2opo2tion, ſay 27 yældeth 512, what giueth 500 the weight of the Falcon, the fourth Proportionall number amounteth vnto 9481. The Cannon therefo2e that ſhall bée able to carrie a Proportionall charge to the Falcon, muſt haue 9481 poundes of mettall, but bycauſe commonly thoſe greater ſo2t of pæces are not ſo maſſie of mettall as indæde they ought to be, the Gunners haue it fo2 a generall rule, that in all pæces aboue ſire ynches of Bo2e, they muſt abate ¼ of their o2dinarie charges.

The ſecond Queſtion.

If a Falconet of three ynches the Bullet, require three pound of Powder for his charge, I demaunde howe mutche of lyke Powder will charge a Cannon of eyghte ynches Bullet.

In this as in the fo2mer, the Rule of Proportion playnelie vſed ſapleth, but wo2king wyth the Numbers reſulting by Cubicall Multiplication, the Quotiente will ſhewe the deſired waight of Powder.

Example.

I multiplie 512 the Cube of 8 by 3 the charge of the Falcon, there ariſeth 1536, whiche diuide by 27, the Cube of 3 the Diameter of the Falcons Bullet, ſo haue I in the Quotient $56\frac{4}{27}$: ſo many poundes of Powder is the due charge of your Canon, but if by the rule laſt taught, you find that the

Canon

Canon hathe not his proportionall masse of mettall, you may accoding to the vsuall Rule of Gunners, abate ½, so will there remayne 42 Poundes, and somewhat moe of Powder fo your Canons charge.

In thys sorte by the Charge of any one péece of Ordinance knowen, you may find out the certayne Charge of all others.

The third Question.

If a Falcon that carrieth poynt blancke 150 pase, at vtmost randon randge 1300 pases, I demaunde howe farre a Culuering at his vtmost randon will reach, that at poynt blancke, or leuell, rangeth 250 pase.

I can not héere, but note the grosse errour of Girolamo Ruscelli Nouarese, who in hys Booke entituled *Militia Moderna*, intreating of greate Ordinance, supposeth, that in all sortes of Péeces, the difference of their vtmost Ranges, should bée in proportion answerable to the waight of theyr Bullets, and charges of Powder, and therevpon deliuereth a Rule by Multiplication and Diuision (the vtmost Randge of anye one péece knowen) to find the same in all other.

In the same Chapter also, he publisheth another Errour, supposing that in one, and the selfesame péece of Ordinance discharged with seuerall charges o quantities of one kind of Powder, that the ranges of the Bullets should alway be Proportionall to the quantities of their charges, o waight of the Powder wherewith they are charged.

In both these cases, the diuersitie of the ranges is compounded of sundrie Proportions, as in a peculiar treatise fo that purpose I wyll declare, and can not by the Rule of Proportion onely bée discouered. But in this Question, the Rule of Proportion precisely serueth, bycause the Poynteblancke and Vtmost ranges in all Péeces whatsoeuer are

R.   indéede

indǽde Proportionall. I multiplie therefoʒe 250, by 1300, there ariseth 325000, whyche diuided by 150, yǽldeth foʒ the fourth pʒopoʒtionall 2166$\frac{2}{3}$, so many Pases shall the Culuerine reach at bys vtmost Randon.

And thus by obseruatiõs vsed in one Pǽce, by this Arte of Pʒopoʒtion, a man maye discouer the foʒce of all o=ther.

Other matters in the Office of the
Mayſter *of the* Artillerie *to bee conſidered.*

I myghte heere adioyne many moe *Queſtions*, touching the weyght, quantitie, and number, of Powder, Shotte, and ſundrie ſortes of Ordinaunce to bee vſed at a *Batterie*: howe to mounte all ſortes of Peeces, to ſtrike anye marke at *Ran-don*: the number of Carriadges, of Ladles, Rammers, Scou-rers, Waddes, Tampions, Cartages, Matches, Barrels, or Laſtes of Powder &c. Alſo, the number of Gunners, Aſſi-ſtantes, Pioners, Smythes, Carpenters, and other *Artifi-eers*, to attende on the *Altillerie*, what numbers of Horſes and Oxen to drawe them, the wayght of all ſortes of Pee-ces, the charges of them, theyr Wheeles and Carriadges. Of thoſe and many other thyngs to the office of the May-ſter of the *Ordinance* apperteyning, as well for the *Fielde* and *Campe, Towne* or *Forte*, as alſo for ſeruiçe on the Seas, I myghte propone an infinite number of queſtions *Arith-meticall*, but hauing in a peculiar Treatiſe of *Artillerie* pre-pared to handle at large all theſe, and many moe rare *Expe-riments* of greate Ordinance, I leaue fartherin this place to wade in that Office.

Queſtions

Queſtions Arithmeticall, concerning the Office of the Treaſourer, the Mayſter of the Victuals, and Captayne of the Pioners.

CHAP. 13.

The firſt Queſtion.

If 17000 pounde be able to pay 5000 Souldyoures for nine weekes, I demaund how much treaſure will ſuffice to pay 30000 Souldyoures for a yeare.

This Queſtion as it ſtandeth vpon a double conſidera- tion of men and time, ſo is it alſo to be double wrought by the rule of Proportion, ſaying thus, if 5000 Souldyoures require 17000, what wil 30000 for like time require. By Multiplication and Diuiſion I find the fourth Proportio- nall 102000 Poundes. Then agayne I ſay, if nine Weekes require 102000 Poundes, what ſhall 52 Weekes, for ſo ma- nie Weekes are there in a yeare. The fourth Proportionall is 589333 Poundes and a Noble, ſo muche Treaſure wyll pay 30000 Souldyours for a yeare.

The ſecond Queſtion.

If 1200 Quarter of Corne ſuffiſe 400 Souldyoures for 9 Weekes, how muche ought to be prouided to ſerue 25000 Souldyoures for 40 Weekes.

Double working by the Golden Rule reſolueth thys Queſtion euen as the former. I ſaye therefore , if 4000 Souldyoures require 1200 Quarters of Wheate, what ſhall 25000, working by the rule of three, I finde 7500 Quarters. Agayne I ſaye, nine Weekes demaunde 7500 Quarters, howe muche wyll 40 Weekes. The fourth

Proportionall refulting by Multiplication and Diuifion, is 33333 ⅓. I conclude therefore, that to mayntepne an Armie of 25000 Souldyoures 40 wéekes. The Mayfter of the Victuals muft prouide 33333 ⅓ quarters of Wheate, in like fort may he forecaft for all other Prouifion.

The third Queftion.

If 500 Pioners can in tenne houres caft vp 400 rodde of trench, I demaund how many labourers will be able with a like trenche in three houres, to intrench a Campe of 2300 rodde compaffe.

This Queftion hathe a farther difficultie than the other two laft paff, bycaufe in the feconde operation the Rule of Proportion muft be inuerfed, and wroughte backwarde, as by the Example fhall more playnely appeare.

Example.

Firft I fay, if 400 rodde of Trench require 500 Souldyoures, what fhall 2300 rodde, hére accordyng to the plaine Rule of thrée, I multiplie the third by the fecond, fo haue I 1150000, which diuided by the firft, deliuereth in the Quotient 2825 Souldyours: then muft I fay for the feconde operation, if in tenne houres 2825 Souldyoures bé able to difcharge it, howe many fhall perfourme the fame in thrée houres. Nowe if you fhoulde worke by the Rule of Proportion direct, you fhoulde finde a leffe number of Souldyoures, bycaufe thrée houres is leffe than tenne houres, but bycaufe reafon teacheth me, that the leffer is the tyme wherein the Trench muft be made, the more Labourers I oughte to haue, I muft inuerfe the operation, multiplying 10 the firft number by 2825 the feconde, and diuide by 3 the third number, fo haue I in the Quotiente 9416 ⅔ fo manie
Pioners

Pioners **muste I haue to Intrenche that Campe in three houres.**

Howe manye vvayes the Rule of Proportion direct, and inuersed, serueth the tourne in these forenamed Offices.

I Thinke it not neeessarie in these matters to propone any more Questions, seying the Ingenious Arithmetricien *by consideration of these may deuise infinite others: As wel in the* Treasurers Office *to supputate the weekely, monthly, & yerely charge of euery Band of Horsemen or Footemen, how differente so euer their payes be, as also the charge of* Ordinaunce, Pouder, Cariages, *and al other sortes of* Munition , *and* Instrumentes *meete to follow any* Army.

The Maister *of the* Pioners *likewise, and* Maister *of the* Vituals *shal neuer be able without this* Arte *to put readily in execution the commaundements of their superiour* Magistrates: *and the more perfection they haue in this* Science, *the more speedily & with lesse staggering shal they be able to discharge their duetie, & shal not neede to rely vpon the direction of any seruant or other hired person, as many do, that being appointed in* Office *wher they should direct others, are fayn first to hire some one or other to direct theselues. Or else that worse is, folowing their own vnskilful brain, shame themselues and ruinate their* Souldiours. *To auoyde therfore such incouenience. I would aduise euery* Gentlema *that wil addict himself to the wars, to make this* Arte *first familiar vnto him, the which he shal finde not only in this* Campe *and fielde seruices to enable him: But also in matters of* Fortification *it is so requisite, that it may by no meanes be spared. As in an especial* Treatise *that I haue begun of those matters I wil make apparant: And in this worke, being meere* Arithmetical, *may not wel be interlaced, the same crauing ayde also of* Instruments *and* Demonstrations Geometrical.*

K.iij.

Here:

Touching the Art of Algebra hovv muche requisite for a Souldiour.

His Art *consisting of infinite varietie of* Equations *in numbers* Cossical, *and also of numbers* Radicall, Rational *and* Irrational, *woulde require a seuerall* Treatise *of great quantitie sufficiently to handle the same, but bycause the subtile* Demonstrations *of the moste curious* Cossical Equations, *and likewise the exquisite* Operations *in surde numbers, are rather for exercise of* Inuention, *& to shew perfection of* Science, *than for any necessitie to be vsed in matters.* Pollitike, *or* Mechanical, *I haue here only briefely deliuered so much therof, as in a* Souldiour *may not be missed, Such a* Souldiour *I say, as shal in al* Militare *causes be able to see with his owne* Eyes, *heare with his own* Eares, *and discerne with his own* Wits, *and not resemble such as runne with others* Legges, *and flye with others* Wings: *such I meane, as if euery* Birde *should pul hir owne feather, like* Esops Daw *might daunce naked. These are no curious* Inuentions, *but plain, easie, requisite* Rules *that here I haue deliuered: The necessarie vse of thē in my other* Treatise *of* Artilerie, Archytecture, Nautical, *and* Militare, *shal more playnely appeare, meaning neuerthelesse, (God sparing* Life *&* Libertie *frō my long troubles) to satisfie also the expectation of such, as flye an higher* Gate, *and wil not stoop at common* Pray: *hauing in the latter part of my* Pantometria, *and in diuerse partes of my* Book *entituled* Alæ seu Scalæ Mathematicæ, *alredie deliuered sundrie* Inuentions *and* Demonstrations, *neuer yet disclosed by anye, which if please them in the meane time, they may peruse. And to such as delight in matter seruisable for the* State *in causes* Militare *(the same being indeede the* Arte *and* Profession *onely or chiefly conuenient for the* Nobility, *and* Gentlemen *of this land) I hope this* Introduction *shal not be vnwelcome: meaning as I see the same gratefully accepted, hereafter to impart the rest, leauing at this time farther to wade in the large* Sea *of* Algebra *& numbers* Cossical.

ARDVA QVAE PVLCHRA.

The thirde Booke.

The conditions and qualities that ought to be in a priuate Souldior.

CHAPTER.I.

Orasmuche as the profession of a Souldior is of al other the most painfull, it is requisite that hée bée of a strong composition of body, to abide both heate & colde, hunger and thirst, trauel and watching, and that when he enter into this course of life, that he put on a resolutió to abide al kind of hardnesse.

Item, that they bée chosen generally from 19. yeares of age till 45.

Also, that he be fitted wyth weapon accoding to his strength. If he be a tall strong man, then is he fitte to vse a Pike: If little and nimble, let him practise to be a good Shot: The meane may vse the Halberde and Blacke Bill.

Item that he be of some occupation, not trayned vppe in ydlenesse: For of al other, the Ruffian that liueth ydely, and séketh the warres onely in hope of spoile, is most vnfitte to make a Souldior, yea, by experience it is cómonly séene, that they are the only cause of Mutinies, and one such is able to disorder and corrupte a whole Band.

That he be skilful in the weapon that he vseth, and haue also the qualitie of Swimming.

Item, that he exercise himselfe continually at ydle tymes among his companions in the Camp, in Runing, Leaping, throwing the Barre, or such like, to make him actiue, and to auoide such idle pastimes as Souldiors cómúly now-adaies

L, vse

vſe,contrary to all good order.

That he be in expences moderate, rather ſparing than ſpending,and his expences to be rather in Armour and gallant furniture, than in exceſſe of meate or drinke.

That he keepe and preſerue his Armour and weapon as one of his members,and that he be deteſted more than a Coward,that ſhal loſe or play away any part therof, or refuſe it for his eaſe and to auoide paines,ſuch a one ſhould not after be ſuffred any more to weare Armor,but either w̃ ſhame and puniſhment be diſmiſſed,or made ſome abiect Pioner.

For a Pikeman the Corſlet is the beſt kind of arming.

And the Harquebuzier with a light Brigandine, or doublet of plate,and a Murriã. The Halberdier may arme either with a ſure Brigandine, or Corſlet. But aboue all other for a day of Battel the old Romane Shield,and the ſhort ſharp pointed Sword, which to execute in a throng of men exceedeth Halbert,blacke Bill,and all other.

He ought diligently to attende, and obediently to execute all ſuch commaundements,as his Captaine or other officer of his Band ſhal enioyne him.

He muſt by continual and heedie practiſe endeuor himſelf perfitely to know the ſounde of the Drumme,whiche béeing wel vſed,ſhould be a very perfite guide of the Souldioures Martche.

Item,that in the fielde he haue alway a ſpeciall regarde to his Enſigne, ſo that if he ſee the ſame in any danger to bée ſurprized by ỹ Enimy, that he endeuor himſelf by al means withoute any reſpect of daunger to preſerue or recouer the ſame, for the loſſe of the Enſigne is not onelye to the Enſigne-bearer, but alſo to the whole Bande a perpetuall ſhame.

The Souldior ought in his apparell & armour to fit himſelfe, that hée bée apte and ready for any maner ſeruice that he ſhal be aſſigned to.

The priuate Souldiour ought not onely to be well able to

vſe

vſe the weapon he ſerueth withall, but alſo ſodaine ly to vn=
derſtande all commaundements of his Gouernors, whether
it be by Voice, oʒ ſound of Drumme, oʒ otherwiſe, and to
knowe howe to maintaine himſelfe in oʒder withoute bʒea=
king array, not only marching, but alſo turning in Troupe
oʒ retyʒing, whiche Diſcipline is almoſt in theſe dayes loſt.
And that Souldioʒ that knoweth his duety howe to behaue
himſelfe in the Camp, in Watche, Scoute, &c. And likewiſe in
Marching, Turning, Retyʒing & Fighting to obſerue the oʒ=
der by his Captaine pʒeſcribed, ſuche a one maye be called a
trained pʒiuate Souldiour, and if he be ignoʒaunt hereof, al=
though he hath bene twenty years in the warres, I account
him not woʒthy of the name of a Priuate Souldiour.

Finally, I woulde haue a Souldioʒ ſo ſoone as he is diſ=
miſſed, & out of pay, that foʒthwith he retourne to his Occupation oʒ foʒmer calling, and not holde it anye imbaſing of
himſelfe to retourne to an honeſt trade of life, conſidering in
the moſt noble gouernement of the Romanes, who in Militare vertue ſurmounted all other, you ſhal finde howe from
the Plough hath bin take a Dictator, who depoſed Conſuls,
guided mightie Armies, ouer-ruled Kings, and yet thought it
no diſgrace to returne againe to his pʒiuate eſtate, vendica=
ting nothing but the Fame and honour to himſelfe, leauing
and contemning the Spoile, and contéting himſelfe with his
owne poʒe poſſeſſions. Such noble Preſidents ought Capi-
taines to lay befoʒe their Souldioʒs eies, and to beate them
from that coʒrupte opinion of Riches and Pleaſure, whiche
are the Enimies of Vertue, and the very oʒiginal cauſes of
the ruine of many ſtately Empires and Common weales.

Tum Caſa parua viros & frugi Menſa ferebat:
At nunc Deliciæ & laqueata Pallatia, molles.
Imbelleſqʒ edunt Fœtus, & luſibus aptes.

L.ij.   The

The office of a Corporall. Chap.2.

AS the Corporal is a degrée in dignitie aboue the priuate Souldior, so ought he also in wit, discretion and diligéce to surmount his Inferiors. There may be of these in euerye bande moe or fewer, at the discretion of the Captaine: but commonly nowe adayes there are assigned to euery twenty ouldiors one Corporall.

This Corporall oughte to kéepe continually companye with his little Troupe committed to his charge, to lodge with them, and prouide for their want, and to instructe them howe to handle and vse the weapon they cary.

He ought to remember perfitly wel how euery one is armed and furnished when he receiueth thé in charge, and to sée that no parte thereof be spoyled, but be preserued neate and trimme.

He ought to looke wel to the behauiour of his Company, not suffering them to vse vnlawful and prohibited gaming, neither to giue themselues to drinking and surfeting, but to spare of their pay to furnish themselues brauely and surelye againstt y Enimy, wher in he ought to vse his chief endeuor.

He oughte not in presence of his Captaine or other superior Officer, to take vpon him more than as a priuate Souldior, and diligently to attend to execute what they shal command, that his example may serue as a president to the rest.

But when this Corporall shall with hys Company be brought to the place where he shal watche, he must prouide himselfe of wood and cole, to haue alwayes light in the body of his watche, and in such sorte to order his Scoutes, that hée may sodainly be able to aduertise his Captaine of any accident that shall arise, & that without disorder and tumulte of his company.

This Corporal also ought to deuise in some sort to Fortifie the place where the Body of his Wach shal stad, in such
sorte,

forte,that vppon the fodaine they bée not enforced vppon the comming of the Enimy to abandon the place.

Also immediately vppon the shutting of the Euening, hée ought difcréetly and warily to order his Scoutes, and fundzy times in the night to reniew them continuing this diligence euen til the dawning of the daye,and therein to employe hys Souldiors of greateft truft.

Also it shal be conueniet, in place of great fufpect,that he appoint double Scouts, matching an Harquebuzier with a Pikeman, that both they may the better be able to defende themfelues being affaulted,& alfo by difcharging of his Harquebuze giue notice to the body of the Watch,that they may giue further aduertizement, and alfo put themfelues in readinefle to abide any fodaine attempt: who ought not to abandon their place, but by the efpeciall licence and commaundement of the Captaine, oz Serieant Maior, and then to retire themfelues in order to the Troupe. And this maye befte be done if the Corporals be alfo interlaced,*Vid.* a Corporall of Shot matched with a Corporal of Pikes oz shozte weapon.

The Corporall mufte alfo fée thefe watches mainteined with Silence, to the end that they difquiet not the refte that fhould take their eafe: and if it happen that any fault be committed,his part is not violently to punifh the Souldioures himfelfe,but to make it known to his Captaine who mufte not neither, as fome rafhly do,reuenge it himfelfe,but communicate the fame with the Marfhall oz his Prouoft, who only haue vnder the General authozitie to punifh.And this due courfe of Iuftice fhal be moze terrible to the Souldioz, and bzéede leffe ill will in them to the Captaine & Officers.

Some vfe vnder euery Corporall two Difniers, whyche the Romanes called *Decanos*, & *Décuriones*,euery of thé had the charge of 9.fouldiors, himfelfe making the tenth,fuche a company of the Romanes was called *Contubernium* or *Manipulus*, the which order is now reuiued among the Spaniards, wherswhereby their souldiors are kepte in verye good order, and their furniture very well and neately preserued.

The duty of a Serieante of a Band.
Chap. 3.

THis Officer ought to be a man chosen of quicke spirite, and actiue body, able both sodainly to côceiue and painfully to execute : and to the ende he be not staggering and astonied vpon new accidents, but prompt & ready vpon euery sodayn to do that to him appertaineth, I would wish that he should passe both the former grades before he be admitted to this.

This Serieant ought perfitly by memorie to know euery Souldior within the Bande, and howe he is armed, who bée Halberdiers, who Pikemen, who Harquebuziers, who Billmen, &c. whiche are well armed, and whiche not, that hée may vpon euery sodain, place them accordingly, arming the vtmost ranckes with the surest men and best furnished.

He ought (when occasion is) to sort his men, euery kinde of weapon by himself, and to dispose them in a certain number by Rancke, as 4, 5, 6, or 7, in a Rancke, accordingly as he shall by hys Captaine or Serieant Maior be commaunded, teaching them to march forward and backward, and also to turne without disorder.

He ought to assigne to eche Souldiour his due place, not suffering them to contend or fall out among themselues for the foremost or better place, but therein to vse this indifferécie, that the best Armed be placed in those places of force, whereby not onely in time of proofe they are more in securitie, and the Band that way the more gallant in shewe: But also the Souldior (to gaine the place of more accompte) wil spare of his pay to arme himselfe the more brauely.

The Serieant also ought, if Victuall want, or Powder, or Shot, or Match, or any other necessary, immediatly to make it knowne to his Captaine or other Officer for that cause appoin-

appointed, and to get it for them as good cheape as he can, &
afterward to distribute the same among the Corporalles, giuing order that it be by them iustly and equally distributed
among the Souldiors.

To this Officer it appertaineth aswell in receiuing as in
laying out to prouide all things for the Company, saue only
Lodging, for that appertayneth to the Harbinger. And therfore me thinketh it were requisite that this Officer shold be
able to Write, for it is harde by Memorie alone to discharge
so many things wel as he shal be charged withall.

He ought alway to accompany the Watche to the place
where they shal stand, and then to giue order to the Corporalles, that they vse greate diligence in sending and setting
their Scouts, and finally, at his departure to giue them the
Watchworde, whyche hee shall receyue from the Serieant
Maior, or Marshall.

He ought with great diligence to attende that the Serie-
ante Maior or his Captaine shal commaunde him, and to see
it speedily executed, rebuking and teaching suche as doe a-
misse, shewing their faultes: but in no wise to strike or beate
a Souldior, for thereby he makes himself worthy of that pu-
nishment the Souldior otherwise for his fault should haue.

He ought himselfe to be throughly wel Armed & appointed, aswel to defend as offend, and after he perceiueth things
wel in order, then ought he to clap himselfe in Array wyth
them, but in such place as he may sodainly steppe forth and
remedy any new disorder, and to returne to his place again,
for the diligent & skilfull vsage of this Officer is of no small
momēt to mainteine good order throughout ye whole Band.

This Officer among the *Romanes* I cannot finde, neyther
in these dayes (if other partes of *Romane Ordinaunces* were re-
newed) should we neede them, but til a perfite reformation
of all disorders these also may be tollerated.

The

The office and duty of the Enſigne
ofa Bande. Chap.4.

As it is conuenient foz euery Souldioz to ſtand vpon hys
credite and reputation, accompting no loſſe of goodes
comparable to a diſhonozable foile:ſo ought eſpeciallye this
Officer to whom the charge of the Enſigne is committed, a-
boue al other to haue honozable reſpect of his charge, and to
be no leſſe careful and iealous therof, than euery honeſt and
honozable Gentleman ſhould of his wife.

Alſo I like wel ſome Ceremony ſhould be vſed in deliue-
rie of the Enſigne, and that he receiue it by Othe in pzeſence
of the Band, & that euery pziuate Souldioz ſhould be ſwozn
alſo to the Enſigne, as amõg ý Romanes it was vſed, when
he was not accounted a Souldioz, but a Theefe oz Robber,
till he hadde taken his othe, and therefoze was their warre
called *Militia ſacrata*.

Alſo he ought to haue with him two oz thzee Aſsiſtants of
the moſte honeſt and valianteſt Souldiozs of the Bande, to
whom vpon any iuſt and vzgent occaſion he might commit
foz a time the charge of the Enſigne.

He ſhoulde marche aduiſedly and couragiouſly, withoute
affectation oz vaine bzauery, not bowing his body, oz vnco-
uering his heade to any, but to the Generall, Coronell, Captaines oz other his betters do reuerence, onely by abbaſing
and enclining the toppe of his Enſigne, moze oz leſſe as
the partie is in degree his ſuperioz.

He ought to know that the Enſigne in ſet Battels oughte
neuer to change frõ the middle of his Band, but in marching
looſe, in Scaling of a Fozte, oz aſſaulting a Bzeache, the Enſigne ſhould endeuoz himſelfe to be the firſt and fozemoſt.

He oughte ſo to behaue himſelfe, that hee bee beloued
of all the Souldoures, conſidering thereby not onelye
his

his owne perſon ſhall be in moꝛe ſafetie when he at-
tempteth perillous exploytes, but alſo the whole ſeruice
moꝛe bꝛauely and honourably exployted, foꝛ the value and
vertue of the Enſigne ſetteth foꝛth the vertue and valoure
of the Captayne and whole Band.

He oughte alway to haue attending on him a Drumme
oꝛ two, to gather his Souldiers togither when nǽde is,
and foꝛ other neceſſarie reſpects.

I thinke good that he be alowed his Horſe with hym in
marching, but his baggage to be caried among the reſt,
with the oꝛdinarie cariage of the Band.

Let the Enſigne be a man of good accompte, honeſt and
vertuous, that the Captayne maye repoſe affiance in, and
not as ſome Captaynes fondlye doe committe the ſame to
ſome of their inferiour ſeruants.

The Enſignebearer ought to be well apparelled, and to
giue the moꝛe reputation to the office, let him alway haue
a Gard to attende vpon the Enſigne, as well in place of ſuſpition, as otherwiſe, and thoſe to bǽ altered at the Captaynes diſcretion.

He ſhoulde be continually Armed, as well when no perill is feared, as in time of danger, to giue example to the
reſt of the Souldyers not to thinke their Armour burthe-
nouſe, but by vſe to make it as familar to him, as hys
Skinne.

The Enſigne ſhould bǽ ſo marked, that both farre and
nǽre the Band may know it from any other in the fielde.

The Enſignebearer ought when the warre is ended, to
deliuer vp to his Captayne agayne hys Enſigne, and although he haue eyther in Battayle oꝛ Aſſault ſo valiantly
vſed himſelfe, that he haue in dǽde deſerued the ſame as an
honourable remembꝛance of his valure, yet ſhoulde he rather accept it by the aſſignemente of his Captayne, than to
ſǽme to vendicate it as due.

M.

This

This Office was also among the *Romanes*, and was called *Signifer*, or *Bandophorus*, a Person nexte their Captaynes, of greatest reputation.

The Lieutenant of a Bande, his
Office. Chap. 5.

THe Lieutenants Office as it is of credite and reputation, so is it also an office of greate toyle and payne, the whiche he oughte willingly to suffer, as well to discharge hys Captayne of toyle, as for hys owne reputation.

He ought not to vendicate to himselfe, any Authoritie, but throughly to vnderstande and reporte to his Captayne the state of things, and from him to take his commission and direction.

He ought franckly and faithfully to giue his Captayne his aduise, as oft as it shall be demaunded, but not to presume to aduize his Captayne vndemaunded, vnlesse it be in case of present perill.

He shoulde in all factions or questions among the Souldioures, be altogyther neutrall, and louinglye to worke wyth them for Pacification, and if he can not by curtesie frame them, let hym communicate the matter wyth hys Captayne, and then faythfully execute hys Captaynes direction.

He ought neuer during the time of seruice to haue Question with any, nor suffer any other to committe the lyke disorder, for that in euerie Band ought seuerely to be proutded for.

It perteyneth to him to ouersee the Sericants, and Corporals, that they doe their duetie, and oftentimes with his owne person to ayde them in setting the Watch. &c.

He ought many times to reuiew y bodies of the Watch, to see how they execute their duties, keeping them Vigilant and diligent to their charge.

He

He ought brotherlie and friendly to vse the Ensigne, ayding him with his aduice, and to be a friendlye Mediator to the Captaine for the inferiour Officers and Souldyoures, for their pay, or any other wante.

He ought both to sée the other inferiour officers to their duetie, and also that they be obeyed without contradiction, and that euery Squadron or bodie of the watche haue theyr Armour, Weapon, &c. sorted and in readinesse.

I hold it also conueniét, that these little Bodies of Gard or watch be not of countreymen or neyghbours, but mixte one with another, to auoyde factions, & other incóuenience.

In absence of the Captaine, he oughte to be obeyed and honoured as the Chiefe, but in presence of the Captaine not to take vpon him any such authoritie.

He should be able to speake well and sensibly, to expresse his mind, that the Souldyoures might vnderstand him, how and what they haue to do.

He may haue his Horse, bycause he hathe occasion more than other to be stirring about the Band, to sée and prouide for all disorders.

His baggage and Prouision should (euen as of euerie other Souldioure) be as little as possiblye he maye, and the same to be caried among the ordinarie prouision, with the rest of the prouision of their band.

This Officer I find not in the *Romane* Armies, neither see I any cause why in these Dayes we shoulde neede them, if the Ensigne and other officers sufficiently knewe theyr duetie.

The Office and duetie of a Captaine.
Chapter.6.

A Captayne ought to consider y he hath the charge of y liues of mē comitted to his hāds, and y if any quaile vnder his cōduct, either by rashnes, or wāt of knowledge; he is
to ren

to render account thereof before the great Iudge. Confidering therefore his important charge, he oughte, before hée
take the same vpon him, to passe some of these former de-
grées, and that in place of seruice, wherby he may finde his
owne sufficiencie or insufficiencie to discharge a place of
such importance.

He ought first to make chopse of sufficient, expert, honest
paynefull Officers. A skilfull Lieutenant, a diligent Serieant,
vigilant Corporals, a godly Priest, a trustie Clearke or Re-
gister, a prouident Harbinger, a cunning Surgeon, with necessarie prouision, and two or thrée good Drummes.

And after he hath brought all his companye togither, hée
shall solemnely deliuer the Ensigne to a chosen man for
courage and honestie, causing him in presence of all the companie to take his oth. &c.

He shall also make chopse of two or thrée of the expertest
Gentlemen of his band, that are well able to discharge any
of the inferiour Offices, these maye be named his Lieutenants extraordinarie, and these he is always to haue about
hym vpon any suddayne, to execute his commaundements,
and ayde his other officers when time shall serue.

The Captaine ought perfitely to know what apperteyneth to the office of euery of the forenamed inferioure officers, that he may presently redresse any thing amisse, and
giue them instructions and order vpon euery new accident,
eyther in Marching, Encamping, or Fighting, what they
haue to do.

He ought alwayes to be in the presence of the Coronell
or Generall, to be enformed of euerie particularitie that is
determined, that he may be the better able vpon any occasion to exployte such seruice as is commaunded, to the honor
of his Coronell, and reputation of himselfe and his Souldyours.

He ought to take order for the carriage of the baggage of
his souldiers, & to sée that they haue as little Superfluitie as

may be poſſibly,to ẛend they may both moꝛe ſpedily march,
and alſo vpon any ſeruice, be rather foꝛwarde to take from
the enimye, than haling backwarde foꝛ feare to loſe theyꝛ
owne.

He ought not to be couetous oꝛ niggardly:neuer to kéep
backe his ſouldiours paye, but by all meanes to ſéeke to get
them their pay,and to his abilitie rewarding them ouer and
aboue, foꝛ by that meanes he gayneth honoꝛ , and maketh
them aſſured to him in any perilous ſeruice.

He ought not to ſuffer any ſouldiour ſaue onlye his pꝛin=
cipall Officers to haue any hoꝛſe : In his officers it is tolle=
rable, bycauſe they may ſometime ſerue foꝛ Light horſemen
to diſcouer ꝛc.

He ought to haue knowledge in Fortification, eſpecially
in the maner of making Trenches and Rampiers,foꝛ as wel
in defending,as aſſaulting,they are often vſed.

He ought neuer to be diſfurniſhed of Lanternes ꝛ toꝛches
foꝛ the night, ſuche as in anye ſtoꝛme oꝛ tempeſt wil burne,
foꝛ many times they maye ſtande hym in ſingular ſteade.

He ſhould alwayes lodge himſelfe among his companye,
ꝛ to endeuour himſelfe to tollerate paines and hardneſſe,foꝛ
it is no ſmall comfoꝛt to the Souldiour to ſée his Captayne
take ſuch part as he doth, and contrariwiſe taking his eaſe,
and ſuffering them to be lodged oꝛ fed miſerablye, bꝛéedeth
him hatred oꝛ contempt.

He ought euerye night that Watche is kepte,to ſende his
Serieãt to the Serieant general, oꝛ other Officer that deliue=
reth the Watch worde, and the ſame to kéepe very ſecretelye
and vſe it warily, foꝛ negligence therein ſometime bꝛedéeth
many miſchiefes.

He oughte to be wel pꝛactiſed in all theſe particulari=
ties, foꝛ a good witte without Practiſe will be to ſéeke in
theſe matters , and if he be not alſo Valiaunt vppon Sud=
dayns, he ſhall neuer be able to execute his duetie.

He ſhould be eloquent,and able compendiouſly and plain=

ly to vtter his minde, and also to perswade and diswade, to recreate and sometimes to prouoke and stirre vp mennes mindes, which oftentimes in these painefull perilous Actions languish, and haue néede of quickning.

He ought not to beate his souldiour, but deliuer him to the Marshal or his Prouost, to haue him punished, for in beating of him, he maketh himselfe hated, and embaceth himselfe, and maketh his Souldiour eyther Mutinouse or abiect.

He ought continually to kepe his Souldiers occupyed in Actions Militare, making them sometime shoote for wagers with the Harquebuze, sometime to wrestle, to runne and to leape in their armour, to march in aray, to cast themselues in a Ring, to retyre in order, and Marching, sodainely to stande, and such like, whereof the Captaine maye deuise infinite varietie, both to delight and also to make his Souldiours perfite, and so farre better spende their time, than in idle lewde pastimes.

He ought not to doe anye thing with his Souldiours, but to haue his Ensigne and his Drumme with him, as well to giue the more reputation vnto the Action, as also that the vse of them may be well knowne, and vnderstande of all the Souldiours.

Finally, a Captaine ought so to behaue himself, as he bée both loued and obeyed of his Souldioures, and that they as wel knowe how to obey, as he to commaund, and that he endeuour himself by al means to annoy the Enimy, and painfully to execute, with all diligence, such matter as he is enioyned by his Superiours, and to feare nothing but Infamie.

Of Captaines there were two sortes among the *Romaines*, the one was *Centurio*, who had charge of .100. mē, the other was called *Comes* or *Cohortis Præfectus*, & had the charge of one *Battaillioune*, vnder whom ther were diuerse *Centuriones*, but one only *Ensigne*, for euery *Centurion* had not his *Ensigne*, as in these our disordered warres is accustomed.

The

The Office and duetie of a Coronel.
Chap. 27.

THe Coronel so soone as he is elected by his Prince or General and hath receyued his Patent and money for the leauying of such a number of men as are to his charge appertayning, ought immediately to make good choyce of his Captaines, assigning such number of men to euerye one of them as he seeth cause, according to the experience and abilitie of the persons.

The more Captaines and Officers that he maketh, if they be able men, the more readilye & the better also shal he take order for the good execution of any seruice, but by such multitude of Officers the Prince shall be ouer muche burthened with excessiue paye, the Wisedome therfore of the Coronel must be in this, that he so distribute & diuide his company, as neyther a conueniente number of Officers be wanting, nor yet the Prince ouercharged.

He ought immediatly after he hath elected his Captains, to deliuer them Imprest mony, to euery one seuerally, suche a portion as may suffise, the whiche he ought to cast before hande, that he maye from his Generall receyue allowance accordinglye : for it is requisite that in the beginning men be not discouraged for want of necessarie prouission, but in suche sort prouided for, that the souldiours may growe into a liking of their Capitaynes. And if the Coronel sometime of his owne, lende to his Captaines, he shall greatlye binde them, and that without any Detriment, considering he is sure to be aunswered the same againe vpon their pay.

He ought also to make him a Lieutenaunte, who besides his own peculiar Bād, ought to take like care of al the Rement that hath bin alreadie declared of a Lieutenaunt in a priuate Bande.

He oughte in like manner to create hym a Sericaunte, such

such a one, as hath bene not onlye of good experience in seruice, but also in this kinde of seruice, for to him it appertayneth sodainely to put men in aray, to alter and change them as the place or occasion shall require, besides manye other partes that hereafter more plainely I wil entreate of in the duetie of the Serieaunt Maior.

He ought also to appoint his chief Harbinger, who ought diligently and indifferently, to assigne fit lodgings to euery Band, and then the Harbingers of euery Band, are to distribute the Quarter appointed, among the Officers and Souldiours of the Band.

In like manner he oughte to make good election of hys owne Ensigne bearer, who shoulde be in value and reputation, a man aboue the rest of that calling.

He shoulde likewise make a chiefe Drumme that shoulde take charge of the reste, instructing them in all particularities that they may both agrée and readily execute any orders by the Coronel commaunded.

He ought to sée that hée want not of Corslets, Murianes, Brigandines, Halberdes, Blacke bils, Pikes, Harquebuzes, Lead, Match, Pouder, and Uictualles that maye suffise for his Regiment, and for al these things that his souldiours be not exacted on in the price.

And aboue al other things, let a Coronel take héede that he be not noted to be a piller of his souldiours, or to play the Marchaunt, making his gaine vppon them, in selling them furniture vpon excessiue prices, for there is nothing so repugnant to the honorable profession of a Coronel, as to be noted Miserable and an Extortor vpon his Souldiours.

He oughte also to examine the choyce that his Captaines hathe made of their Officers, and if they bée good to allowe them, or else not.

If his Regiment amount to the number of a fiue or sixe thousande, then shal he not néede other horse than those that are allowed to the Officers of the Bandes, who may serue
the

the tourne for difcouerie &c. But if his Regiment be fmal, J woulde wiſhe he had an hundred horſe at the leaſte, whiche ſhould be Harquebuziers, for winning a paſſage frõ Peſants & vnarmed mẽ, or fetching in a Booty, they ar ſingular good.

He ſhould haue about his perſon certain wiſe expert valiaunt Gentlemen, that be able vpon any ſuddaine, to execute any of the inferiour offices, and that are able both quickelye to conceyue, and playnely and ſenſibly to vtter any newe accident, or thing whatſoeuer that he ſhal ſée. And theſe oughte he to haue continually about his perſon, to execute ſuch matter ſpéedily and faithfullye, as he ſhoulde commaunde them. Theſe maye be named his Lieutenauntes extraordinarie.

It is alſo the part of the Coronel to aſſigne euery Captaine, what kinde of weapons his ſouldiours ſhall vſe, and albeit the preſent cuſtome be, that euery Captaine ſhoulde haue in his Bande both Pikes, ſhort weapon, & Shot, yet do J holde it farre better, that they ſhoulde haue in their Bande but one ſort of weapon. For by that meanes in euery ſeruice the Captaine ſhould alwaye accompany his own Souldiers, whereas otherwiſe if he wil abyde in the ſtanding battayle with his Piks, he muſt committe his Shot to be ledde by an other, and his ſhort weapon by a third, which is an extreame diſorder: and nothing ſo much encourageth the Souldiour, as to ſée his Captaine a companion of his perils, and the contrary no leſſe diſmayeth him.

Finallye he oughte alwayes to attende in the preſence of the General, to honor and obey him, and to refuſe no paynes in exployting his commaunded ſeruices, for thoſe paines are honorable, they get thée Fame and make thée immortal.

This Officer was alſo in vſe among the *Romaines*, & was then called *Drungarius*, *Tribunus Militum*, and *Chiliarchus*, & commonly in euery front or face of ther battayles they had two or three of theſe *Tribunes* or *Collonels*, and the gouernor of the whole front was named *Turmarcha*, *Merarca* or *Tur-*

N. *marum*

marum Præfectus, comparable in some respectes to the *Captaynes* of the *Vaward* Battayle and *Reerewarde*, sometimes in these dayes vsed.

The office of the Scoute maister.
Chap.8.

This Officer in the auntient Romaine wars was neuer in vse, for they would neuer admit any Watch without the trenches of their Campe, but obserued this order, that euery night one third parte of the Armie remayned armed, the other two thirdes toke their rest. And this armed parte they diuided into foure quarters, and appointed to euerye Watch of the night one quarter, whiche wente and walked continually about the trenches of the Campe, to heare and sée if they coulde discerne anye noyse or stirring nighe the Campe, the other thrée quarters resting in the meane tyme armed in the place of assembly. And when the firste Watche of the night was ended, then departed another quarter to ý reliefe of the Watch, and the quarter that had watched, retourned to the place of assemblye. And thus they continued relieuing the Watches till daye. So that the enimy coulde neuer approche their Campe, but they founde one third part in Armes, who were able to kéepe them play, till the rest had put themselues in order. But after the Militare discipline grewe to corruption, and that Souldioures neglecting honor and securitie woulde no longer abide the hardnesse and seueritie of the Antique Discipline, they inuented this kind of Forraine scoute, that the paynes of a fewe might leaue the rest at ease. But what mischiefe hath and may therby ensue, Histories will shewe vs, and common reason maye sone teache vs. But séeing among manye other corrupt customes of these our times, this is now also in all our Christians warres vsed, I wil briefely shew his office, as among vs it is now a dayes accustomed.

The

The Scout maifter oughte diligentlye to viewe and note rounde about the Campe, al the places of fufpecte where Enimies in the night time might approch, that he may accordingly afterward difpofe of his Scoutes, and therefore hée fhoulde attende vpon the high Marfhal at fuche time as hée goeth to make choyce of a méete plat to encampe on. And then to fpeake his fanfie, touching the conuenience or inconuenience of the feate, in refpecte of due place for the Scoutes.

Alfo as foone as the Trumpet foundeth to the Watch at nighte, he muft immediately repaire to the Lieuetenaunt of the Horfemen, requefting him to affigne him a competente number of Horfemen, to attend vpon the Scout that night, and then muft he giue them charge vpon pain of death that none of them abandon theyr places, till the Difcouerers be come into the fielde, and haue taken theyr places.

The beft order for the placing of the Watche, that I haue noted, is thys. Firffe he fhall fet the ring Watche rounde abouts the impalement of the Campe, *vid.* a Bill, a Bowe or Harquebuze, and a Pike, and euery one a Pike length from another: then without them, certain little Troupes, fiue or fixe in a troupe, of footemé of different weapon, *vid.* Bowes, Harquebuziers, Pikemenne and Short weapon, and thefe Troupes alwaye to fend forth a couple, whereof a Harquebuzier alwayes to be one, and thefe to prye and hearken what they can difcerne. Again without this Foote Scoute, other fmall Troupes of Horfemen, fiue or fixe in a companye, and thefe likewife to difpearfe themfelues abroade to difcouer what they can. And if they happen to fée or heare anye thing, prefently to reporte the fame to the Foote Scout, & one or two of the Foote fcouts, to repaire to the Scout-mafter, who is (if it bée matter of importaunce) to open the fame prefently to the high Marfhal.

Befides all this, in tyme of fufpecte it were requifite

that

that a Stande watch be maintayned within and aboute the Ordināce. But bycause that appertaineth not to the charge of the Scout Maiſter, I let it paſſe.

It is requiſite in the long colde winter nights, to relieue the Wacch fiue oʒ ſixe times at the leaſt in a night, the ſame moʒe oʒ leſſe as y̌ Scout maiſter, ⁊ other pʒincipal Officers ſhall thinke méete, foʒ the better pʒeſeruation of the people.

Alſo in the moʒning ſo ſoone as the Trumpet ſoundeth y̌ reliefe of the Watch, he muſt repayʒe to the ſayde Lieutenauntes tent, there to receyue by his aſſignement, a conuenient number of Hoʒſemen to ſcoure that daye, and then ſhall he giue oʒder vnto ſome, to ride to the higheſt hils to biewe rounde about what they can eſpie, and others to the baleys and other obſcure paſſages, woods, oʒ ſuche like, and to ride one from another a good diſtance: ſo as if one chāce to be ſurpʒiſed by y̌ enimy, yet the reſt maye eſcape ⁊ bʒing intelligence therof. ⁊ ſo ſoone as y̌ Scout maiſter ſhal receyue any aduertiſemēt by the ſcourers, he ſhal foʒthwith repayʒe to the high Marſhal, ⁊ enfoʒme him of euery particularitie.

He ought in placing of his night Watches oʒ Sentinels, to vſe great conſideratiō, firſt in ſetting his little Troupes, oʒ bodies of the watch in ſome places of ſtrength, ſo as they may be able, when the enimie ſhal appʒoche, to make reſiſtaunce and defende themſelues, till ſuche time as the Campe maye put themſelues in armes. And beſides theſe troupes, he ſhal giue oʒder y̌ two oʒ thʒée ſhal walke foʒthe one waye, ⁊ as many moe another, ⁊ if they happen to ſée any matches light, oʒ heare anye noyſe, foʒthwith one to repayʒe to the body of the Watch, ⁊ ſo to the Scout maiſter, ⁊ the other to ſtay til they can moʒe plainelye perceiue what the matter is. And it ſhal be alwayes good to match ſome Harquebuʒes togither with Pikemē, as wel that they may be the better able to defende themſelues, as alſo by diſcharge of their Harquebuʒe, to giue warning to the reſt, if any one of them ſhould happen to be ſurpʒiſed by the Enimy.

This

This Officer ought to be both diligente and paynefull, considering howe greate a charge dependeth vppon these Scoutes, no lesse than the preseruation or destruction of the whole Camp, and therefore he ought continually both day and night, eyther himselfe in person, or by some other of greate trust in his absence, from time to time to peruse and examine the order and demeanor of these scoutes and scourers, giuing order for reformation of all that he shall finde amisse, and so soone as he shall receyue anye intelligence, forthwith to aduertise the Lord high Marshall.

The *Romanes* had their Difcouerers called *Scultatores*, or *Speculatores*, and others, called *Campiductores*, whiche were the guides or Conductours of their armie, by the moft conuenient wayes and paffages : but of any fuch peculiar officer permanente, I haue not red in the *Romane* Stories.

The Office of the Serieant Maior.
Chapter. 9.

This Officer is alfo of reputation, and ought to bē a man of great courage, and well experiéced, that he be not difmayde with the Terror of the enimies prefence : for the moft parte of all his actions are to be exployted euen in the face of the Enimie.

He ought to be a man of liuely fpirit and quicke Inuention, that he may fuddaynely perceiue, and quickly conceiue the nature of the Scituation and order of the enimies array, altering and difpofing accordingly of his owne.

He ought euerie day to repaire to the Lorde High Marfhall, or the Lieutenant Generall, to receyue direction in what fort their pleafure is the Armie that day fhal march.

He ought to receyue from the Lorde High Marfhall a perfite Rolle of all the Bandes, and in euerie bande what number of fhort weapen, what Pykes, and what Shot, and the fame to haue alway aboute him, that if anye wante, he may

may admonish the Muster Mayster and Treasourer there
of, eyther they may be supplyed, or hys Roule refourmed.

The Serieant Maior after he hath from the Marshall, or
Lorde Lieutenant Generall recepued instruction in what
sort the Battayle shall martch, he must presently sort euerie
kinde of weapon by it selfe, and then draw them forthe in
Hearses or Sléeues, 5. 6. or 8. in a rancke, as the prescribed
order shall require.

He ought so to place euerie band, ý their Captayne may
be with them, to directe and animate them: but this is impossible to be done in these our warres, where euerie small
Band is diuided into seuerall weapōs, so that the Captains
in time of seruice can not accompany his owne Band, contrarie to all good order and Discipline.

He ought when a daye of seruice commeth, to goe wyth
the High Marshall to biew the place where the Battayle
shall be foughte, and there to speake his opinion howe the
matter should be ordered, and ý done, obediently to execute
suche directions as he shall recepue from his Superioures.

To this Officer it apperteyneth, so to sort his Souldyours,
that the best armed impale the rest, and that the face and
flanckes of your Battayles be well armed with Pykes, the
Ensignes well garded with Halberdes, the tayle enclosed
with the Carriadges, Wings of Shotte on eyther side, and
those Wings more or lesse accordingly as the place is larger or streighter, stronger or weaker, on the one side, or on
the other. These Wings represent the Flanckers in Fortification, and ought as orderly to Flancke and skoure before
the face of the Battayle, as Bulwarkes dothe the Curtane
of a Towne or Forte.

He must also so order the Forlorne hope in ý front of hys
Battayle with new supplies out of the Wings, or from betwéene the Battayles, that the Front of the armed men be
neuer left naked or vncouered, till both Battayles come so
nigh, as they be readie to ioyne and crosse their Pikes, then
                                                    may

may the Shotte retire eyther to the Wings, and so to the Ordinance, or betwéene the Battayles to the Carriadges.

If the Souldiours be rawe and vntrayned men, it maye be tollerated to put them into one mayne Square well impaled with Pikes, and so committ it to one brunt. But if the Souldiers be trained in such sort, that they can in sight both martch forward if they preuaile, or retire vpon aduantage, and yet mainteyne perfitely their Arrayes, then by no meanes committe the Battayle to one hazarde of Fortune, but after the old Romane manner make thrée or four seueral Fronts, with conuenient spaces for the first to retire and vnite himselfe with the second, and both these if occasion so require, with the third. The Shot hauing their conuenient lanes continually during the fight to discharge their peces, which shall make an incredible spoyle of the Enimie.

It is also the parte of this Officer, in time of rest, when the Enimie is absent, to cause the Bands to assemble, and to put them in sundrie sortes of standing and marching Battels, to reduce them sometime into smal Squadrons, of 400 or 900 in a battayle, more or lesse at his pleasure, & to cause these Batalliōs to march forwarde swiftly or slowly accordding to the stroke of the Drumme, to stay and to retire in perfite measure, no lesse assuredly, than men are taughte to daunce by the sound of Musicall instruments. And whē they can perfectly doe this, then cause them suddaynely to make any Flancke a Front, or turne entirely togither, as if it wer one bodie, without breaking their Aray. And when they cā do this, albeit they neuer saw ÿ enimie in the face, yet may they be tearmed Trained Souldiers, & if they wāt this skill, albeit they haue bin in twentie battels, and twenty yeares in the wars, I hold thē raw souldyers, & vntrayned Bands.

It is also a poynt of great cunning to make a Squadron martch vppon one corner, mayntepning still his Square fourme: and this and such like varieties in marching, albeit they be not in seruice so necessarie, yet doe they bryng

the

the Souldyours to a singular readinesse, and are farre better, and more commendable pastimes, than Dicing and Carding, whiche the famous Romanes in their Campes would neuer tollerate.

He must consider the difference betwéene marching and standing battels. And this is a generall rule, that there is no Battayle méete to march, but only the Battayle that is square, or compound of Squares. All others, as the Lunula, the Triangle, the Pentagonall, and Hexagonall Battailes, the Circular, and Ouall, with infinite others that easilie may be inuented, neuer serue to anye vse, but onely in fixed and immouable Battailes, for presently in marching they disorder.

These kinde of immoueable Battayles though of themselues they are smally seruiceable, considering in all encounters continuall motion is required, and it is not possible to trayne men to that perfection, as being raunged in such forme of battayle, shall not presentlye in marching breake their aray. Yet for exercise of men, I holde it verie requisite, that the Sericant Maior both know how, & also often do put his Souldioures into these fashions of embattapling, causing thé suddaynely to change frõ Triangle to Square, from Circulare to Lunulare, and thereby bryng them to suche perfection in these vnnecessarie hard cunning toyes, that the other playne seruiceable fourmes may séeme most playne and easse.

This Officer ought before hand, to premeditate and cast in what sorte with most facilitie he may bryng his men to order of battayle, cõmitting to the peculiar Sericant of euerie bande, the charge to drawe thé forth in Sléeues, and so cause one to march close vp by another, till all the battailes be furnished, placing the Ensignes alway and Drummes in the middle ranckes of the battayles

He néede neuer take care to order his Shot in any forme of Battayle, but only to put them into certayne Wings, and
everie

euerie VVing to be diuided into sundzie petie Troupes of twentie oz fiue and twentie men a péece, and euerie of these troupes to haue a Leader oz Corporall. And to maynteyne a Skirmish, first one Cozpozall martcheth forth, and bzingeth to the face of ý enimie his little Troupe, who presentlie discharging, retire themselues: and in place of them, another Cozpozall with his companie presents himselfe, continuing this ozder of Supplie, till the firste haue charged agayne : and in this sozte maye they continually maynteyne Skirmish without intermission. But the place being large, it shall be requisite oft times to presente manye of these Troupes at once to the face of the enimie, who hauing deliuered their Volue of Shot, shall marche away as is befoze sayd, and others supply their place. And this kind of discharging and supplying, maye verie well in the open fielde bée mainteyned in the Ring martch, so as the Head shal be sure alwayes to haue charged, befoze the Taile haue discharged: and thus in a Circulare martch, the Skirmish all day continued.

In playne ground he should neuer turne out any shot to the Skirmishe, without certayne sléues of Pikes to garde them vpon the retreate from the charge of Hozses, and also certaine small Troupes of shozt weapons, as Swozds and Targets, Halberts, oz suche like, to backe them, if at anye time they should come to the Swozd, oz ioyne peale meale with their Enimies : and such of the Romanes were called *Vindices*. But if euerie shotte hadde likewise at his backe a light Target to vse with his Swozd whé he saw occasion, it were much the better.

Our Englishe Bowes also to gall and disozder a Troupe of Horse, may serue to very good purpose, but they must bée garded with Pikes, &c. euen as I haue alreadie declared of other Shotte.

Item, the Serieant Maior by his office, is to appointe euerie Captayne his place, some in the Fronte, some in the

Rerewarde, some to leade Shotte in the Wings, other to guide the Forlorne hope, and all these are accordingly to put in execution his commaundement.

He ought to be allowed certayne experte Gentlemen, to attende alway vpon his person, to employ this way or that way, as occasion is offered, and these should be men of suche perfection, as are able presently to conceyue, and liuely to expresse any thing y is vpon suddaynes to be done, touching the changing of the Arrayes, or other seruice whatsoeuer.

For the better execution of these, and many other importante Seruices to this Office aperteyning, if the number of Souldiours be great, it is very requisite that this Officer haue knowledge in Arithmetike, whereby he maye suddaynely for all formes of Battayles, resolue howe manye Ranckes, and how many in a Ranck to frame the Battailes, what number of Pikes, of Halberds, and Shot shal be requisite, how many Sléeues or Hearses euerie Battaile may be resolued into, how many Ranckes of Pikes in the Front or Traine of those Hearses, and how many Ranckes of Halberds to gard the Ensigne. Also vpon sight of the ground, to consider whether it be able to receyue suche multitude of mé: Also what forme of embattayling may best agrée vnto it. In these and many other questions, méete and necessarie for the consideration of a Sericant Maior, I haue before shewed how requisite Arithmetike is.

Some vse to create two or three or moe *Serieants Generall*, but in truth this officer among the *Romanes* needed not, for euerie *Colonell* for his owne bandes was a *Serieant Maior*, and for ordering of the whole, in the day of *Battaile*, the *Generall* himselfe discharged it, and all inferioure officers knew so wel their duties, that such officers would among them haue bin reputed meere superfluous.

The

The office of the Lieutenant or Generall of the Horsemen. Chap. 10.

His Officer hath vnder his charge all sorte of Horsemen, as well the light Horsemen and Demilances, as the Men at Armes, and Barbed Horses, seruing to breake into a Battallion of Pikes, or to backe the other Horsemen being repulsed. And albeit I meane not in this place particularly to entreate of the seuerall charges of euery Captayne of light Horsemen, Demilances, and men at armes, yet thus muche I thought good to note, that a Captayne of an hundred men at Armes may be compared with a Coronell of footemen, and other Captaines of lighte horsemen, with the Captaynes of footemen, subiecte to the Coronell. And as it is the parte of the Coronell to haue a speciall regard to the arming, lodging, and trayning of his footemen: so is it the dutie of the Captayne of men at Armes, to foresée, that neyther they be disfurnished of their Horse and Armour, with other necessaries, ne yet vntrayned in al such militaire exercise as to their profession is agréeable. And this Lieutenāt is to ouersée the actions of these Captaines, and to giue order in what sort, in what place and time they shall exercise their bands.

He ought immediately after his entring into charge, to haue a Roule of all the Bandes committed to his gouernement, with the names of their Captaynes, and then to peruse their furniture, if it be good to allow thereof, otherwise to make the High Marshall and Generall priuie of the default, that it may be amended.

He shall giue order to the Captaines vnder his charge, that frō time to time they aduertise him of their defaultes, eyther of mē, horse, or armour, ỹ he may prouide for supply.

He must dispose his seuerall sorts of Horsemen in seueral troupes, the Barbed Horse by themselues, Demilāces by themselues, ẽ of his lighte Horsemen, the Hargabuziers in a seuerall troupe from the rest. And héerein I can compare this Officer with the Sericãt Maior, bicause he is to receiue his direction from the Generall, or High Marshall, euen as he doth, and then accozding to the order resolued on, to dispcse of these Bands.

He is to appoynte whiche bands of Horse shall go to the watch or scouradge, ɇ must accozdingly prouide, that they which watch the night, may rest the next day ɇ night, and others that haue rested, supply their places, in such sozt, that freshe men may alwayes be employed in the seruices, and the wéeried to take their rest, for neyther Man nor Horsse without their conuenient rest can continue any long time.

Also so sœne as ẙ Trumpet shal sound in the mozning to make readie the Horse, he shal fozthwith repaire to his Generals Tent to know his pleasure, and then immediately to set fozth his Generals Standerd, and cause all the Horsemen fozthwith to repaire to that place, and as euery Captayne shall come, he shall cause them to put their bands euery one after his Standerde oz Guidone, into a certayne number of Ranckes, that the said Lieutenãt may readilie at euery suddaine draw fozth any nũber of any sozt of hozsemé that hée shall be requited by the Generall oz High Marshall.

The Lieutenant ought in the mozning, to giue notice to such hozsemé as he intendeth shal watch ẙ night ensuing, to the end they may fǽde and spare their Horses that day, and also rest thẽselues, that they may ẙ better be able to do such seruice as they shall the night following be enioyned.

When the high Marshall goeth to biew the grounde to encamp bpon, it is the Lieutenants dutie to select a conuenient Band to attend bpon his person, and to appoynt suche a Companie, as maye afterwarde take their rest, and fǽde their Horses, till suche time as he shall deliuer them to the Scoutemayster at night, who then shall enioyne them what to doe all the night after, and shall also deliuer them theyz Watchworde.

This.

This Lieuetenaunt ought all the daye, whiles ȳ Battels martche, diligently to note the oꝛders of euery Band, and if he ſée any diſoꝛder, foꝛthwith to ſende foꝛ the Captaine, and cauſe him immediately to ſée it redꝛeſſed. Also at night whē the armie entreth into the Campe, the Lieuetenaunt ſhall ſtil cauſe the Hoꝛſemen to kéepe the field, til al the Fœtemē be encamped, then maye he enter with his Bands of hoꝛſe oꝛderly, cauſing firſt one Band to enter, and al the reſt kéepe the fielde, and when they haue their conuenient place, then another Bande to enter, and ſo oꝛderly to place themſelues. Wherein the Lieuetenaunt is to foꝛeſée that the laſt Bands be not woꝛſt lodged, but ſuche conuenient place left, as they haue no iuſt cauſe to complayne.

He oughte alſo to giue oꝛder that the Scowrers come not out of the fielde , till the Trumpet ſounde to the Watche at nighte, noꝛ then neyther, till ſuch time as they ſhal perceyue the Scout oꝛ Sentinel to be come from the Campe , and to haue takē their places in the field : Then may they returne into the Campe.

He ought alſo to aſſigne a ſufficient number of Hoꝛſe to attende on the Forrage maiſter, to guarde and defende the Forragers, which Hoꝛſemen muſt not come out of the fielde, till all the Foꝛragers be retourned to the Campe with the Forrage maiſter. Then ſhal theſe Hoꝛſemen reſte, and not Watche neyther that nyghte, noꝛ Scoure all the nexte day.

He is alſo to appointe a reaſonable Conuey of Hoꝛſemē, foꝛ the ſafetie of ſuch as bꝛing victuals to the Campe, to ſée that no violence oꝛ iniurie be offered vnto them, and ſo oꝛder the chaunge of his Hoꝛſe in theſe ſeuerall ſeruices, that ſome be not ouer burthened, and others ouer-ſpared, but ȳ matter ſo indifferently vſed, that men haue no cauſe of murmuring oꝛ repyning.

In making of Rodes with Hoꝛſemen only, he ſhould firſt ſende out light Hoꝛſemen, Argoletiers, and ſuch like, to diſ-

couer the Enimie : then to diuide his Launces into diuers
Squadrons, & one of them to follow another a good distance.
Of euery side of these massie Squadrons shoulde be a prettie
distance from them one ranke of Argoletiers. In this sort if
one Squadron happen to be broken, yet shall another make
hed vpō the Enimy while they may retire and Troup again:
which is the onely safetie as well of Horssemen as Footemen.

And albeit in the day of seruice it is the part of the High
Marshall himselfe to giue order in what sort, and with what
Troups the Charges shall be giuen or receyued : it is also
the Lieutenants parte as well to giue his aduise, as also to
be a Leader in al these Actions.

He ought therefore to take great regarde to the grounde
where he meaneth to giue the Charge, for if he charge in
Troupe, the falling of a fewe Horsse in the formost rankes
may dysorder and foyle the whole Troupe.

He musse not giue charge before the Fronte of his owne
Footmen, for it hath bene seen that Horssemen being repulsed, haue bene forced in vpon their owne Footmen, and dys-
ordered them. Let the Horsse therefore charge vpon the
Flanck of the enimie, and diligentely attende if by any accident they can perceyue any breaking or opening in the side
of his enimies Battaile, & then sodenly to charge that breach:
for as Horssemen shall smally preuaile vpon Footmen well
ordered, so vppon any small dysorder, they cary with them
certaine victorie.

I like wel the maner of the Germaines, who keep always
their maine Troupe standing, and cause only one ranke frō
the Front to charge, and the same being repulsed to retire to
the tayle of the standing Troupe, and thē another to charge
and retyre to the Tayle, as the former, wherby they maintayne the whole Troup in ful strength, til they see the Footmen swaye or breake, and that they Horsemen enter.

Then presently they backe them with an other rancke,
and

and thofe againe with another, til they ſée cauſe epther to folowe with the whole Troupe, oʒ to ſtaye. And this is the
ſureſt and moſt oʒderly foʒme of charging of al others. Albeit ſometimes alſo the Ruyters vſe to Whæle about with
their whole Troupe, and euery ranke one after another to
giue the Enimye a volue of their Piſtols.

For execution of Iuſtice on ſuche as are offenders in a-
ny Bandes of Hoʒſemen : Albeit in ſome Countries it bée
vſed that euery Captaine of an hundʒed men at Armes may
cal vnto him certaine of the chief of his Band, ȝ heare and
determine all cauſes, and offences by any of his Bande committed, yet ſurely I holde it moʒe conuenient, that all matters concerning life, be heard by the high Marſhal, who
maye cauſe to ſitte wyth hym the ſayde Captayne whoſe
Souldiour is to be adiudged, and ſuche other of the ſayde
Bande as to him ſhall ſéeme méete, and the Souldiour con-
demned to death, to be executed by the ſayde Band, euen as
the footemen are: and by the ſame kinde of weapons that the
offenders vſed.

This Officer among the Romaynes, was called *Magi-*
ſter Equitum, or *Præfectus Equitum,* he had the charge
both of the Barbed horſes, called *Cataphractos,* and alſo of
the lighte Horſemen, which they named *Expeditos Incur-*
ſores. His Office was not only in the fielde to ſee his Captaines vnder him to doe their duetie, but alſo in the
Campe to trayne theyr Bandes in all Militarie exerciſe
and Actiuitie.

The

The Office of the Maiſter of the Ordinaunce. Chap.ii.

THis Officer being one of the principall Officers of the fielde, hauing the charge of the Artillerie and Munition, ought to be a man of greate learning and experience. His Experience ſhall make him readie to conceyue and exployte many particular Actions, wherein a very good witte without trayning ſhall ſtagger and be amazed. Learned he ought to be in Hiſtories, to cōſider of manifold Stratagemes that by other noble Souldiours haue heretofore bene vſed: The ſundry ſortes of Engins to aſſault & defende: of Bridges to paſſe Waters, and other ingenious inuentions for conueying of great Ordinaunce ouer Marſhes: But eſpecially he ought to haue exquiſite knowledge in the Mathematicals, conſidering thereby he ſhall be able certainely to Shoote at al Randons, to conuey Mines vnder the earth to anye Curtaine, Bulwarke, or other place that he determineth by violence of pouder to rente in péeces: to ſupputate and forecaſt what quantity of ſhot, pouder, &c. ſhall be requiſite for anye Batterie, or other exployte: To ſet out in due proportion euerye particular Fortification, of Campe, Towne, or Forte, where Ordinaunce is to be vſed, whiche cannot poſſiblye without knowledge in theſe Sciences be ſufficiētly diſcharged. And that Maiſter of the Ordinaunce, that is ignorant herein himſelfe, and truſteth to ſkill of others, ſhal be abuſed by audacious preſumptuous perſons, that taking vpon them the knowlege they vtterly want, will ſhame theinſelues, diſhonor him, and foyle the Enterpriſe.

He oughte immediately vppon the receypte of his charge to cauſe an Inuentorie to be made of euery ſeueral thing, as well to render account therof, as alſo to conſider whether he haue ſufficiēt of euery ſort of Munition to ſerue the tourne.

To

To this Officer appertayneth a Lieutenaunt, and certain Clarkes, in wages, who are to attende inferiour causes, rendring accounte of al their doings to the Maister of the Ordinaunce.

To this Officer it appertayneth to foresée, and from time to time to prouide, that there be store ynough for al kinde of necessaries to the Artillerie appertayning, as Whéeles for Ordinaunce, Axeltrees, Ladles, Spunges, Bullets, Chayne-shotte, Crossebars, Corne pouder, and Serpentine pouder, Mattockes, Shouels, Crowes of yron, Hande axes, Engines for the mounting of Ordinaunce: Graund Maunds, or Gabbions, little Handebaskets, Roapes, and all other Carte-ware.

Item, to haue such Gunners as are not only skilful in the readie maneging of their Péeces, but also in the making of Trunkes, Baules, Arrowes, and all other sortes of Wilde-fire, and for the continual supply of them, they ought to haue in readinesse greate stoare of Sulphur, Salte Peter, Rosine, *Calx viue*, Lintséede oyle, and common lampe oyle, Pitche, Tarre, Camphire, Waxe, Tutia, *Arsenike*, Quick-siluer, and *Aqua vitæ*. Hereof let them frame Baules of fire to burne in the water, Cressets and Torches that stormes or winde can not extinguishe, murdering Bullets to be shot out of great Morter péeces, and such like.

Item, that euery péce of Ordinance haue his conuenient number of Horsse or Oxen to drawe the same, and Carters also to guide and kéepe those Beastes.

Item, that euery Péece haue his Gunner or two to attende theron, to charge, dyscharge and mount the Péece, also to wadde and ramme, to cleanse, scoure, and coole the Péeces when they are ouerheated: & for this purpose they shall haue in readinesse Spunges, Uinegre, and colde water. &c. And for these Gunners, there should be one Master Gunner to ouerséé them all.

R. Item

Item that if anye Bande in the Campe want Powder oʒ ſhotte, the Maiſter of the Ordinaunce vppon requeſt of the Captain, is to giue oʒder that his Clarkes deliuer the ſame, taking a Bil of the Captaines hande foʒ their diſcharge, the which Bil muſt at the pay daye be deliuered to the Treaſurer who is to ſtoppe ſo much vpon the pay of that Captaine and his Bande.

To this Officer it alſo appertayneth to haue in readineſſe certaine Boates made foʒ the purpoſe with flat couers of ſquare Planckes, whiche chayned togither maye make ſuddainely a Bridge, to paſſe an Armye ouer any water: He ought not to be diſfurniſhed of Cables, and Anckers, to let fall in anye ſwifte oʒ violent ſtreame to holde the ſayde Bridge.

The Maiſter of the Ordinaunce is alwayes to haue attending vpon his charge a ſufficient Band foʒ the Guarde of the Artillerie, & alſo Pionersto make redy the way foʒ his Cariages, and to entrench the place in the Campe that ſhall be (by the Prouoſt Marſhall) aſſigned foʒ the Munition.

Item, that there be of Wheele wrightes, Carpenters, Coopers, Smythes, Bowyers, Fletchers, Maſons, and ſuche other ſkilſull Artizans with all tooles neceſſarie and needeful, to pʒeſerue, repayʒe, and make all ſuche things as to the Artilery and Munition appertayneth.

In the fielde, whenſoeuer any day of ſeruice is, it is the Office of the Maiſter of the Ordinaunce, to ſelect a conuenient place to plant his Oʒdinaunce, as well to annoye the Enimy, as alſo to be in ſuche ſoʒt guarded and foʒtifyed that it be not ſurpʒiſed of the Enimie.

Item, in the Campe, he onely oughte to giue oʒder foʒ the planting of the Artilerie, and Fortifycation of the Flankers. And that the Oʒdinaunce be planted to the beſt aduantage, and alſo to foʒeſee that the Mayſter Gunner and other Gunners do theyʒ duties whyche doe appertayne to theyʒ
Office,

Office.

Item, in the besieging of anye Towne or Fort, he onlye oughte to dispose and giue order for the planting of Artilerie, to make the Batterie, and to foresée that they be wel fenced with Gabbions and Rampiers of earthe, and so placed, that the Curtaine maye with most spéde and least charge be battered and ruinate.

Item, that al suche Peeces as are vpon any mounte within the Towne planted to the annoyaunce of the Campe, maye be dismounted, and the Flankers cut of before any assault be giuen.

Item if there be any possibilitie to approch the Towne by Myne, the Maister of the Ordinaunce only ought to giue order for the accomplishing of the same. And the Captayne of the Myners and Pionors is to folowe hys direction.

Finally this Office is of great reputation in the fielde, and the execution and exployting of great seruices dependeth therevpon. But bycause it is neyther possible nor conuenient that the Maister of the Ordinaunce shoulde attende all these thyngs himselfe, he maye committe inferioure causes to the execution of hys Lieutenaunte, reseruing alwayes to himselfe the disposition of the great and most important.

I Mighte here adioyne sundrye *Tables*, and collections of al sortes of great *Artillerie*, what Bullets, Wadders, Rammers, Ladles, Leuers, & Barrels of pouder, what Wheels, Axeltrees, Chaynes, Corde, and all other arming, and furniture for Carriages, to euery kinde were conueniente to bee hadde in readinesse, what Oxen and Horse to drawe them, *Pioners*, Carters, and Gunners to attende them: *Instrumentes* and Arte to mounte them, *Gabbions* to defende & guard them, wyth sundrye receytes and compositions of Trunkes, Arrowes, Balles, Barrels, and other Engines of fireworkes &c. both for *Offence* and *Defence*. But hauing in my Treatise of *Pyrotechny*, & great *Artilerie*, prepared at large to handle euery of these particularly, and to supply the wantes of this Office fullye, meaning in this Treatise but generallye to touch and giue a taste onely in each degree of our wants and imperfections. That our *Nation* may not alwayes rest drowned in this ignorance, and secure dreame of *Antique valure*, while all oure neyghbours rounde aboute vs *Arme, Traine* and *Fortifie*. Till I may haue time to finish that *Treatise* I leaue further to entreate of this matter.

Of the Maister Gunner.

THe Maister Gunner is but an vnder Officer appertayning to the M. of the Ordinance : And his office is, to see all the inferior Gunners to do their dueties, to be skilful and ready in their charging, dyscharging, cooling, leuelling, and mounting of the Ordinance : and to haue in readinesse Bullets & Pouder, Ladels, & Spunges, to Wad, Ramme, Coile & charge the Peeces, also to peruse the Carriages, and Wheels that they be strög, and the Peeces themselues, that they haue no bony combes or flawes in them, whereby they should be in daunger of breaking. To haue in store Crosse barres, Chayneshotte, Cases of Haileshot in manner of Cartages, Trunkes and Baules of Wildfire, with Artificiall Barrels of preble stones charged with pouder to throwe into ditches, or to defende a breache vpon any sodaine attempte : These and such like are matters for the M. Gunner to occupie himself in, and to make proues of them in presence of the M. of the Ordinance, that he may see the effect and violence of them.

These Officers among the *Romanes* were not, bicause *Ordinance* is newly inuented, and to them vnknowen, but

in stead

in ſtead of *Artillerie*, they had *Arietes, Scorpiones, Baliſtas*, and *Arcubaliſtas*. They had alſo *Teſtudines, Turres*, and ſuch like *Engins*, whiche in beſeeging of Townes, and other ſeruices, they vſed. But all theſe are nowe out of vſe, and ſerue in deede to ſmall purpoſe. The force of *Ordinance* being ſuche, as the *Fortification* of Townes in theſe dayes is cleane contrarie to that of the *Antiquitie*, and *Romane Præſidents* therein can nothing pleaſure vs.

Of the Lord high Marſhall in the fielde
or Camp. Chap. 12.

The Office of the High Marſhall is of greate impoꝛtance, and hath the direction of the greateſt, and moſt impoꝛtant matters in a Campe. To him appertepneth the true adminiſtration of Iuſtice, the hearing and determining of controuerſies, and the puniſhing of diſoꝛders. And therefoꝛe as he oughte of himſelfe to be a man both graue, wiſe, learned, ꝛ thꝛoughlp well experiecced in Martiall affaires, ſo is it alſo conueniente foꝛ him to haue about him men of iudgemente, ſkilfull in Militare diſcipline, and lawes of a Campe, readilie to reſolue of euerie queſtion, accoꝛding to Equitie and Iuſtice.

Farther, this is to be noted, that the particular Lawes of anp Prouince, ought not to bind the Souldiour in the fielde, but euerie Campe oughte bp pꝛudent conſideration of the Generall, and his Counſell, to haue lawes ſet downe and decrǽd, yea, and the ſame to be publiſhed bp open Proclamation, that all the Camp map haue notice thereof.

Some thinke it neceſſarie alſo, that not onlp euerie Captayne and Coronell ſhould be ſwoꝛne to the ſaid Lawes, but after the old Romane manner euerie particular Souldiour at his entring into pap to take his Oth. Foꝛ ẏ which cauſe, the Romane warfare was tearmed *Militia Sacrata*.

P.iij.   The

The high Marſhall ſo ſoone as he hathe receyued of the Generall the names and numbers of all the Bandes of Horſemen and Footemen that are in the Armie, he muſt learonedly proportion and caſt what ſcope of grounde wyll ſuffice to encamp them, with all their Prouiſion, Carriadges, Munition. &c. wherein he ought to obſerue ſuche a diſcrete meane, that neyther for want of due roome the Souldyers be peſtered, nor by ouerlardge ſpace, the Campe not ſufficiently Fortified.

This being one of the moſt important matters that the high Marſhall hath to conſider of, it ſhall be requiſite for him to haue knowledge in Geometrie and Arithmetike, and to haue in readineſſe ſundrie Plattes, Models, and formes of Campes, whereby he ſhall ſuddaynely reſolue for any number or Scituation, what forme and quantitie of Camp is moſt conuenient, and preſently ſtake it out, aſſigning due place for euerie Regiment of Footemē and Horſemen, Carriadges, Ordinance, Munition, and euery particularitie, as hæreafter ſhall more playnely be declared.

When the Armie ſhall remoue, the High Marſhall muſt firſt giue order to the Maiſter of the Ordinance, that he ſet forth the Artillerie, with al the Carriadges, Munition. &c. then the Mayſter of the Victuals, and Carriadges afterwardes.

Afterwarde he muſt giue order to the Serieant Maior in what ſort he will haue the Battaile to martch that day.

Item, he muſt giue order to the Skoute mayſter whyche way he ſhall ſend his Vanquerers to diſcouer, if all be clæere, who muſt from time to time giue intelligence what Occurrents he diſcouereth.

The High Marſhall muſt aſſigne euerie Battayle hys Guide or two, to conducte them the beſt and moſt eaſie wayes.

Item, he muſt appoynt ſome conuenient number of Pioners to attend vpon ẏ Ordināce to clæere the wayes for thē.

The

The High Marſhall when he goeth to view the groundes where he intendeth to Encamp, may by his authoritie take ſuch number of Horſemen, as he ſhall thinke conuenient, and then is he to cōſider, that there be nigh at hand Wood, Water, and Forradge ynough for the Armie. And if he intende long to lodge in that place, then muſt he make hys Camp the larger, and prouidently conſider that euerie Regiment haue his conuenient place. That the Tentes be not pitched nigh the Ring of the Campe. That there be large places of Aſſemblie within the Camp. That it be well Entrenched and Fortifyed, whereof I will more particularlie ſpeake in the Deſcription of a Camp.

For lodging of Horſemē, eſpecially in a running Camp, it is not amiſſe to imitate the Ruyters, who commonlye alwayes lodge in ſuch Cloſes, as they finde enuironed wyth trées, or quickſet hedges and ditches, placing their Horſes in due order round about the field, two paſes one from another, with Rayles betwéene them, leauing all the voyde ground in the middle for the Captaynes Tentes, and Cabbins for the Horſemen.

In this ſorte in a field of two or thrée acres, I haue ſéene a two hundred Ruyters verie commodiouſlie lodged, wyth Rayles or Poles betwéene their Horſes, and Boowes about them, to defende them from the wind. Some with Hales ouer them, to kéepe them from the Rayne, their Saddles, Bridles, and all other their Furniture hanging vpon Poles readie by them, neatelye kept, and blacked, their Mangers alſo before them. For al ſuch neceſſaries the Ruyters carrie with them in their Carriadges, beſides, little Whéelebarrowes to carrie away their dung, ſo that their Campe is no leſſe cleane and orderlie, than a Princes Stable. A faire ſtréete they alway leaue betwéene their owne Cabbins, and their Horſes.

The

The Ruyters manner of Lodging.

They haue certaine Troupes of their Seruants, whome they call their Kneyghts, and these Troupes alway attend, that so soone as the Marshall hath limited their Quarters, they departe immediatelye to the next Woods, for Poales, Boowes, Stakes, and other necessaries, to build their Camp, Stables, and Cabbins. Other goe for Forradge, that before the Armie approch, their Lodgings are alwayes in readinesse. To euerie twelue Ruyters commonlye, there is allowed a Wagon with four Horse, or to fixe, a Carte, with two Horse: and their Kneyghts are about one thirde parte of the number of the Horsemen.

The Lance Kneyghts also encamp always in the fielde verie stronglye, two or three to a Cabbonet, theyr Pykes and Armour standing vp by them in readinesse, and so orderly placed with streetes so conuenient and cleanly preserued,

ned, that their Camp is no lesse holsome than strong.

I haue sene aboue.3000.of these *Lanceknyghts* lodged in three or foure acres of grounde, whiche *Proportion* differeth not much from that of the olde *Romanes*.

The high Marshall, aswel for the ordering of Scoutes as al other matters of importance in the Campe, is to giue order, and at the setting of the Watche his Trumpets oughte first to sound, and then all the residus of the Trumpets in order to answere euery one in his seuerall Quarter. And in the morning all the Trumpets should assemble before the Lord Lieutenaunte Generals Tent, and there to sound the reliefe of the Watche: But no man vppon paine of death muste remoue from his charge till the Warders be come oute : then may euery man departe to his reste.

He ought to giue order, that such as come to victuall the Campe be well vsed, and truely paid, and that vpon Victuall some reasonable price be seazed : and that suche a place bée assigned for the Butcherie, as annoye not the reste of the Campe.

Item, in the field at a day of seruice though there be a Generall of the Horsemen, yet is it the place of the High Marshall to serue there as chiefe, and to appointe into how many Troupes the Horsemen shal deuide themselues, and whiche shal Charge, and which stand for their Rescue.

Item, if any Prisoners be taken in the fielde, they ought forthwith to be Enrolled in the Marshals Booke, and then if any man make claime to any other mans Prisoner, the Marshal as Iudge to determine who shall haue him, and for euery Prisoner brought into the Martialsea, and enrolled in the Marshals Booke, his Fée is. 8. ß.

He is also to haue of all Booties taken in the fielde and broughte into the Camp the third part: But aswell for this, as other his Fées, they are by the Generall to bée limitted at the beginning, as shal be thought reasonable.

M.   Finally,

Finally, the High Marshall oughte to be a man of suche perfection, that he know the duty of euery inferior Officer, and be able to refourme their misdeeds, and that of his own knowledge.

He shoulde make choice of a good Prouolte, to whome he may committe the handling of smaller matters, alwayes retayning the greater causes, and such as concerne Life, to be heard by himselfe: And for his greater reputation, and to be knowen from other Officers, he shoulde haue in the field borne before him a Cornet.

And forasmuch as to this Officer chiefly the execution of Militaire Lawes appertayneth, I will briefly here adioyne suche Offences, as by law of Armes are to be punished with Death: For other that are not so haynous, the Marshal may by imprisonmēt, or otherwise at his own discretiō chastise.

Offences to bee punished vvith paine of Death in euery Camp or Armie.

Frst, *whosoeuer committeth or conspireth any* Treason *againste the* Generall: Or *giueth any aide to his Enimies:* Or *vseth any conference with the Enimie without expresse licence from the* Lieftenaunt Generall, *or one of the* Lieutenauntes *of the* Horse *or* Foote Campe.

Item, *whosoeuer shall discouer any matter of* Counsell, *whereby any inconuenience may ensue:* Or *shal sende any letter to the Enimie without leaue of those* Lieutenants: Or *shal receiue anye importante* Intelligence, *and doth conceale it from the* Generall *to any ill intente.*

Item, *whosoeuer shal fly from one* Campe *to another:* Or *beeing taken of the Enimy shal not escape when he may: prouided alwayes that after he hath giuen his faith to be true Prisoner, it shal be lawful for him to obserue it.*

W.hosoeuer *shal Trayterously or Cowardly render vppe anye* Town,

Town, Forte, *or other place committed to his charge, being founde by due triall, that it might haue bin kept.*

Whosoeuer *shal break any truce with the Enimies:* Or *shal lay any violent hands vpon any Officer his superiour, vnlesse it be for defence of himselfe, his life being in apparant peril.*

Whosoeuer *shal kil his Souldior vpõ malice without iust cause:* Or *kil any other of the* Camp, *otherwise than in his owne defence.*

Whosoeuer *shal go about to make any* Mutinie: Or *shall disobey the soundes of* Trumpet *or* Drumme *in time of seruice, especially when they are made vpon paine of* Death.

Whosoeuer *shal forcibly abuse any woman :* Or *take any spoile without leaue:* Or *enrolle hymselfe in twoo Bandes:* Or *passe twice in one* Muster *:* Or *parte from Bande to Bande without licence of the chiefe Officers: For the* Captaines *haue no aucthoritie to giue such leaue.*

Whosoeuer *shal not folowe his* Ensigne: Or *abandon the place he is assigned, whether it be in* Field *or* Watch: Or *shall sleepe in the* Scoute *:* Or *shal reueale the* Watcheword *to the Enimy.*

Whosoeuer *being placed in* Watche, Scoute, *or other place of importaunce so behaueth himselfe, that by his default the* Camp *is sodainly without notice assaulted :* Or *being appointed to the keeping or defending of the* Trenche, *or* Breache, *and shall abandon the same.*

Whosoeuer *shall spoile any* Victualler *or other person oute of the* Camp, *being not of them that are declared* Enimies: Or *shall play away his* Horse *or* Armour, *wherewith he is enrolled:* Or *flying awaye shall loose the same :* Or *anye other waye by his owne default shall be of that his Armour dissurnished.*

Whosoeuer *quarrelleth with any Souldior placed in* Watche, *or other places of importaunce :* Or *runneth to any quarrell with any other Armoure or Weapon than his Sworde :* Or *being thrice commaunded to cease, and departeth not.*

Whosoeuer *retireth not immediatly vpon the sound of the* Retreit, *maketh noise when* Silence *is commanded :* Or *passeth ouer any Wal or* Rampire *forbidde: Or lodgeth any strãger in his* Tent *without leaue from the chief Officer:* Or *fayneth himselfe ſicke whẽ he is commaunded to the Battel, or other importante ſeruice :* Or *abſenteth himſelfe wilfully from the* Militare exerciſes.

For *al other inferiour faults, as Dicing, Carding, Rayling, Slandering, Quarreling, beaſtly vſing themſelues within the* Campe, *and ſuch like, the* Prouoſt Marſhall *is to puniſhe them, who ſhould haue* Tipſtaues *attending on him, preſently to apprehend ſuch diſordered perſons, and to carry them to Warde.*

The 𝔐aiſter of the Pioners, the Trench & Mine 𝔐aiſter, are Officers wholly depending on the High Marſhall, and are not to doe any thing of themſelues, but onely to ſee that their companies and people committed to their charge haue their Furniture in good order, and doe the worke they ſhall be enioined diligently. But of themſelues without Warrant theſe Officers can do nothing.

I Find not among the antient *Romanes* any Officer vnder the *Generall* of ſo greate reputation as this Lorde *Marſhall* now is, for albeit they had *Cenſores* and *Anticenſores*, which in ſome ſorte may be compared with the *Marſhall* and hys *Prouoſt*, in reſpeＣt that they made choyce of the grounde to encampe the Armie on, and alſo diſtributed the *Quarters* & *Regiments*, yet were they far in dignitie inferiour. And thys *Officer* was firſt deuiſed (as I iudge) to ſupply the imperfeＣtion and ignoraunce of the *Generals*, and after continued for their eaſe to disburthen them of thoſe *Cares*, wherein the *Romane Generals* tooke greateſt *Fœlicitie:* And were then no leſſe iealous that anye inferiour perſon ſhoulde participate wyth them of thoſe honourable trauels, than *Generals* are now deſirous to disburthen theſelues of al cares and paines. And althoughe togither with the Ruine of the *Romane Monarchie, Militare Diſcipline* in *Europe* for theſe thouſand yeres hath bin in effeＣt quite extinguiſhed, yet ſome worthy perſons in all ages haue ſought ſomwhat to reuiue the ſame: As may appeare by the *Prince* of *Conde,* and *Admiral* of *Fraunce,*

whoſe

whoſe *Diſcipline* for their *Campe*, brieſely I haue thoughte good here to adioyne, bycauſe it ſomewhat ſauoureth of the *Antique Romane.*

The Lawes and Ordinances for go-
uernment of the Armie vnder the conduct
of the Prince of *Conde*, in the ciuil Warres
of *Fraunce.* Chap.13.

The othe miniſtred to all the No-
bilitie, and Gentlemen Captaines,
and others within their Armie.

YE ſhall *ſweare before the Liuing God, that for the cauſes and occaſions contayned in the Proteſtations made by the Prince of Conde, yee ſhal aduenture your Bodyes, Lyues, and Goodes, and al other meanes that God hath giuen you, vnder the charge and obey-ſaunce of the ſaide* Prince, *whome yee knowledge as Chiefe, and Conductor of this* Armie, *yee ſweare and promiſe your obedience to all, whatſoeuer ſhall by the ſaide* Prince *or ſuch as beare charge or office vnder him be commaunded, to obſerue duly al ſuche* Mili-tare Ordinaunces *as by them ſhall be preſcribed for the gouerne-ment of this* Armie *&c.*

THe Prince hauing by experience founde, that no Armie can be wel led and gouerned, if it be not well ordered, ru-led and diſciplined, and the ſame not poſſibly to be done, if at the firſte good Lawes and Ordinances be not preſcribed: And if ſuche things haue bin obſerued among them that had no knowledge of God nor of true Religion, much more oughte theſe things to take place among thoſe that make profeſſion of True Religion, who ought to be as a Precedent and Pat-terne to others in al right and Iuſtice, and not in diſordered

and

and dissolute liuing, as in our laste warres, and euen verye lately also hath bin séen: For this cause ý Prince being willing to discharge as farre forth as in him lyeth the duty and charge that God hath committed vnto him, being duly thervnto called, after he had assembled the moste notable and best able Gouernors, Captaines, and other of the best iudgement and vnderstanding of all suche as were to be founde in his Armie, hathe agréede vppon these Articles and Ordinaunces ensuing, the whiche his pleasure is shall be precisely in euery pointe obserued and kept vnder the paines in the same articles contayned.

And if any suche be, as peraduenture shall not like to allowe of them, the Prince meaning not to compell any, but by voluntarie obedience, giueth them frée warning to retire themselues out of hys Armie, meaning that all suche as shall remaine vnder his conducte shall inuiolably obserue al these his Lawes and Ordinaunces, the whiche he will sée indifferently executed vpon al sortes, withoute regarde or respect of persons.

And firste the Prince enioyneth al such persons (whether they be Horsemen or Footemen, Gentlemen or others) if they be not of ý nūber of those that haue Charge, that they Range and Enroll themselues vnder some one Cornet or Ensigne, there to take their Othe as is appointed for them, and that within sixe dayes after they shall approche the Armie: Otherwise if they be founde in default after the saide time, al their Armour and Horse to be to the proper vse and benefite of him or them that shall bewraye the same to the Prince or to the Marshals of the Campe.

And all suche as shall cause themselues to bée enrolled, shal be bound to obserue and performe theyr duty in Watch, Scoute, and Scourage, accordingly as shall be ordayned by the Marshals of the fielde, their Captaines, or other Officers hauing charge ouer them, vpon paine, if they disobey, to bée dispoiled of theyr Armour, the whyche shall bée confiscate
togither

togither with theyr Horſes to the vſe and benefite of their Captaines.

Neither maye they that haue taken their Othe departe from their Cornets or Enſignes without the leaue and permiſſion of their Captaines the whyche they muſte make apparant befoꝛe they be elſewhere receiued: And if any ſhal do otherwiſe, the Captaine from whom ſuch are departed, ſhal cauſe them to be bꝛought befoꝛe the Prince, who ſhall take ſuche oꝛder foꝛ recompence betwæne the Captaines, as to him ſhal ſæme mæte: And touching the offendours, their Horſe and Armoure ſhall be confiſcate to the vſe and commoditie of the Captaines from whome they are in ſuch ſoꝛte departed.

And to the end no man be bnawares ſurpꝛiſed with thys daunger: The Prince commaundeth all his Gouernors, and Captaines to cauſe dayly theſe Oꝛdinances to be publiſhed, and made knowne to ſuche as from time to time ſhall newly come into the Armie, and Range themſelues bnder their Cornets oꝛ Enſignes.

And bycauſe ſome Captaines maye happily abuſe oꝛ yll handle their Souldioꝛs: The Prince permitteth them notwithſtanding their ſaide Othe, bppon iuſt occaſſon to demaunde leaue of their Captaynes to departe: And bpon refuſall oꝛ deniall, to repayꝛe bnto the Prince, who hearing either parte, will take ſuche oꝛder as ſhal ſæme bnto him reaſonable.

And to the ende all things maye with good oꝛder be directed: the Prince willeth and commaundeth, that this Othe by him oꝛdayned, ſhall monthly be renued, and that if then there be any Gentleman oꝛ Souldior that will abandon hys Captaine, it ſhal be lawfull to declare the ſame befoꝛe hym that ſhall be appointed Commiſſioner to take the Muſter and giue the Othe, who maye gyue Licence to the ſame Gentleman oꝛ Souldiour, if ſo be that he finde no Doubte oꝛ Difficultie by reaſon whereof he thinketh it conuenient

to

to referre the same to the Prince himselfe, oz suche as shall expzessly from the Prince be assigned to examine suche Debates and Differences : And in the meane time, the Prince expzessly fozbiddeth all Captaines and Gouernors to pzactise oz subozne one anothers Souldiours.

And to discouer suche as shall departe the Armie without leaue, the Prince enioyneth and commandeth the Commissioners that shal reuiewe the Musters, monethly from time to time to pzesente vnto hym the Roules wherein shall bée wzitten the Mames and surnames, togither with the abode of euery person, to the ende such as shall be found culpable of such e faulte and infidelitie, shall publikely be denounced and declared Enimies of God, and traiterous fozsakers of the cause.

And fozasmuch as the Prince desireth nothing moze thã to cleare his Armie of Uagabonds, and suche vnnecessary people, he expzessly fozbiddeth al persons to folow his army, that are not Enrolled, and ozderly aduowed; the which they shall sodaynely make manifeste whensoeuer it shall bée demaunded by signed Certificates. The Footemen and Horsmen to haue their Certificates from their Captaynes: the Lackeys, and seruantes from their Maisters, and the Victuallers, Merchantes, and Artificers, from the Prouostes and Campe-maisters, vpon paine that whosoeuer shall after thzée dayes ensuing the pzoclamation of the Pzemisses, be founde wythout the said Certificates, he shal be hanged and strangled.

And to the ende euerye Captayne and Gouernour may the moze easily render an accompte of such as shal be subiect to their charge, being very hard to command moze thã 100. hozse, The Prince willeth ɬ ozdayreth, that no Cornet shal haue any greter number: And neuerthelesse, if any Gentleman by reason of the good wil which shal be bozn vnto him, shal haue any greater numbers to folow them, The Princes pleasure is, they shal diuide them accozding to that rate of

hundzeds

hundreds, appoynting their Lieutenants accordingly. And as for Foote bands euerie Ensigne to cõteyne 200 souldiers.

The Prince also expressely forbiddeth all that serue in his Army, to go to any seruice or enterprise without leaue, vnder payne if he be a Captayne, to be depryued of hys charge : if he be a priuate Souldiour, to be depryued of hys Horse and Armour, and banished the Armie. As he doth in like manner forbid all souldiours of his Armie to abandone their Cornets or Ensignes, ordeining ỹ such as shal be found from their said Cornets or Ensignes spoyling, forradging, & Praying, to be corporally punished as robbers & Théeues, and breakers of these Ordinances, and their spoyles, togyther with their Horse and Armour, to be to the vse of suche as shall bring them before the Prince to aunswere their offence.

And for as muche as this Warre being of an other Nature than others Warres, ought also to be ruled after another fashion, The Prince commandeth, that all Prayes and Booties shall be brought and put into the hands of such persons as shall be by him deputed and assigned, to the end the commoditie and benefite thereof resulting, may reasonably be diuided and imparted to the mayntenance of the Warre, and reliefe of such as shall haue néede thereof. Prouided alwayes, that if any such Enterprise be made, as the Souldioures giue Battayle or fight for it, that then the Bootie shall be diuided, according to the auntient lawes of the warres. And for al other Prayes and Booties, one Third to remayne for the Captaynes and Souldyoures, and the other Two Thirds for the publike cause and maintenance of the Armie. And if there be anye that do conceyle anye parte of the Bootie, the Prince hys pleasure is, that some honest, present, and consideration (according to the value of the thing) be bestowed on the reuealer of the faulte, and the concealer to be corporally punished as a Thiefe, and Enimie to the cause.

R.   The

The Princes pleasure is also, that all compositions of Villages, Castels, and other things of like nature and qualitie be committed into the handes of hym or them that shall by the Prince bée therevnto deputed, to bée by them converted to the vse before mentioned.

And for as muche as great abuse is often committed in the taking of Booties, the Prince ordeyneth, that nothing shall be reputed, or declared Bootié, vnlesse it be verifyed and duely approued by those of the Counsell, and made apparant eyther by some sutch as were taken, togyther wyth the Bootie, or by some other good and sufficiente Testimonie.

And to the ende all suche thyngs (of what nature soeuer they bée) that shall bée recepued, shall truely and faythfully bée handled and distributed, The Prince wyll chose some one principall personage of good qualitie and reputation, who shall kéepe a Roule or counterpane of all suche things as shall be recepued.

And bycause there are manie that entertayne a greater trayne than they ought, vnder coulour that they liue at Discretion, the whych full ill agréeth with the profession of oure Religion, and ingendreth greate confusion in an Armie, and sometime danger and losse, by reason of the great superfluitie of baggadge. The Prince exhorteth and admonisheth all Gouernoures and Captaynes, be they Horsemen or Footemen, to bée diligente and caresull in searching and examining the state of thynges, and not to permitte anye to haue a greater trayne than is necessarie. &c.

And for as muche as all disorders do principallie growe by reason of the excessiue traynes and baggadge that Footemen and Horsemen carrie with them, who commonly doe vse to robbe and steale Horse, and other labouring Beastes, to carrie theyr Pilladge. The Prince willeth and commaundeth, that none shall haue more than one Ser-

uant

nant o2 Lackey fo2 euerie th2ée Souldyoures at the moff,
and thofe alfo to bée bound to followe the Enfigne as well
as they2 Maÿfters, and not to ftray from they2 Quarters,
vppon payne of hanging and ftrangling. Neÿther fhall it
be lawfull fo2 them to ferue they2 turne with Ho2fes,
Dxen, Affes, o2 fuche lyke, the whÿche hée declareth,
and o2deyneth to bée confifcate and fo2fayte, if they2
p2oper maÿfters, tó whome they ought indéede to bée re-
fto2ed, doe not challendge them. Onely vnto Captaynes
and Officers fo2 they2 owne p2oper vfe and commoditie,
the Prince doth allow the vfe of them.

And to p2euente and méete wyth fuche abufe as maye
growe by diffimulation o2 wincking at fuche faultes,
the Prince hys pleafure is, that thofe hys commiffioners
alfo fhall Mufter and reuiew the fayde Traynes and Baggadge, and refo2me and cutte off that fhall féeme vnto
them fuperfluous, and of them to make a Regifter, to
the ende thereby mo2e eafilie the offences committed a-
gaynfte the p2efcribed o2ders, maye be difcouered. And
in the meane time, confidering the mifchiefe and inconuenience that doth growe by fuche robbing and ftealing
of labouring beaftes.

The Prince o2deyneth, that fuche as fhall be atteynted
and conuicted to haue robbed o2 ftolne anye of that fo2te
of Beaftes, fhall bée feuearely and rigo2ouflie punifhed
as Traytors and enimies of the publike caufe, vnleffe they
bée ficke o2 hurte, and in that cafe they are enioyned to
make their Captaynes p2iuie, who fhall p2ouide fo2
them.

And fo2 as muche as at the place where the Armie
fhall firfte affemble, they do commonly determine of they2
Enterprifes, and debate many other impo2tant matters fo2
the fafetie of the Armie marching and lodging, The
P2ince commandeth all thofe that haue charge, to be there

present, and also the chiefe of euerie Troupe, or at the least their Lieutenants or Cornets euerie morning to giue their attendance at the lodging of their Chiefes of the Armie, whether it be of the Battaile, or Vawarde, there to vnderstand what is for them to do.

The Prince his pleasure also is, that all suche safeconduites as shall by him, or the Admirall be giuen, shall be respected and regarded vpon payne of death.

The Prince also expressely forbiddeth all persons to robbe or spoyle any Victualers, or other commodities that shall bée broughte into hys Campe, vppon payne of death.

And to the ende that no man shall pretende ignorraunce of these Ordinances, the Prince hys pleasure is, that the chiefe Gouernoures and Captaynes of hys Armie shall euerie wéeke cause them to be publikely redde, both in the Battayle, and Vawarde, and in all partes and Quarters of those Regiments, and in all other places of Garrison, or assemblie of Souldioures, and the same to be inuiolably obserued in euerie poynte, accordyng to their tenure and true meaning, and the offenders to be seuerely for example punished, withoute altering, or innouating any of the lawes and Ordinances of the Kings Maiestie, as well touching the ordering of Menne at Armes, as Footemen, all whyche ouer and besydes these presentlye published, the Prince commaundeth duely to bée obserued and kepte.

These Lawes ordeyned by the *Prince*, the *Admirall*, and other famous Souldyoures then lincked with them, I haue heere publifhed, not to the ende euerie *Generall* fhoulde bee bounde to the felfefame *Lawes*, but imitating theyr *Policie*, to affemble theyr principall Officers, *Coronels*, and *Captaynes*, and before they martch forwarde, to decree fuche *Lawes* and *Ordinaunces* as

may

may feeme moft fitte for the gouernemente of fuche people as fhall ferue vnder them, mittigating or increafing the paynes, as fhall be founde meete. And the fame to be publifhed, and by *Othe* receiued, as in this *Precedent*, and in the honorable auntient *Romaine warres*, was alwayes accuftomed, whereby fuch extreame diforders, and fpoyle of men fhal be auoyded, as alwayes is feene in thofe *Regiments*, where *Difcipline* is neglected, and men onely by *Difcretion*, or rather by *Fantafie*, directed and corrected.

The Office of the high Treafurer.
Chap. 14.

This Officer is of greate reputation, and hath to his charge committed the payment of Coronels, Captaines, and al other Officers. He ought in the beginning to receyue from the Generall the true number both of Horfemen and Footemen within the Campe oʒ Armie, and by perfit computation to make a boke howe muche is due euery moneth to euerye Colonel, Captaine, and other Officer, as well foʒ themfelues as theyʒ Bandes.

He ought to make his Proportion of paye wel knowen to the General, whereby the Generall mighte accoʒdinglye make pʒouifion that money be not wåting to pay the Souldiours.

He oughte to conferre with the Maifter of the Victuals to fée how he is furnifhed, and accoʒdinglye to difburfe vnto hym, that hée bée not deftitute of conueniente pʒouifion.

He ought in like foʒte to make allowance (when néede
fhal

ſhall be) to the Maiſter of the Ordinaunce , foꝛ ſupplying his ſtoꝛe of Munition as he ſhall ſee cauſe , by reaſon of conſuming of the olde, oꝛ any impoꝛtante ſeruices to bee done.

He muſte conferre with the Maſter maiſter, to ſee howe the Bandes be furniſhed, what Souldiours be ſlayne, when and how many, and how and when ſupplyed: deliuering pay to euery Colonel oꝛ Captaine, accoꝛdingly, keping the Warrantes oꝛ notes of their hands foꝛ his diſcharge.

He ought alſo at the pay day to conferre with the Maiſter of the Ordinaunce, to ſee whether he haue any Bils from the Captaines oꝛ Colonels, foꝛ any Pouder, oꝛ other Munition receyued, and to deduct ſo much in their wages.

Greatly maye this Officer be ayded by Arithmetike, without the which it ſhal be an extreame toyle to make true computation of ſuch variety of Payments , oꝛ befoꝛe hande to Preconiecture of all ſoꝛtes of pꝛouiſion and Munition what ſhall be neceſſarie. But by ayde of that Arte the moſt difficult doubtes that can therein ariſe ſhal with facilitie be reſolued and diſpatched.

This Officer ought alſo to be a man of greate Wiſedome and wel experienced in Millitare Affayres, bycauſe he is vſed in Counſel where he is to ſpeake his Opinion in al exploytes of impoꝛtaunce although they concerne not direct ly his Office.

This Officer the *Romaines* alſo had, named among them *Quæſtor*, he had the charge of the publique Treſure, & was of the like reputation and account in al reſpects to this Officer of ours.　　　　　　　　　　　　　　　　　　The

The maister of the victuals.

THe Maifter of ye Victuals ſeemeth to be an Office altogither dependent on the Treaſurer, hauing nothing elſe to doe but to prouide and take charge of the Prouiſion in the Campe. And as corne or other victuals ſhal grow ſcant, to make the Treaſurer priuie, that order may be taken for further ſupply epther by money or ſending forth the Forrage maiſter to take it by force, and againſt the pay day he muſt bring in his booke of accountes to the ſayde Treaſurer, and there receiue allowance accordingly.

Of the Muſter Maiſter.

THe Muſter Maiſter alſo maye be accounted an Officer as it were dependent on the Treaſurer, for that hys dutie is nothing elſe but by often reuewing of the Bands, to ſee how euery Captaines Band is furniſhed, noting the Defaultes from time to time, and the Supplyes, and thereof to make a perfit booke, exhibiting the ſame at the pay day to the Treaſurer, that allowaunce may be made to the Colonels & Captaines accordingly.

HEre I had thought to haue adioyned certayne *Tables*, of the allowaunce for the Leauie and entertaynment of Souldiours with their Officers, according to the *Almane*, *Spaniſhe*, *Frenche*, and *Italian* cuſtomes, as well for *Cauallerie*, as *Fanterie* : But by conference I finde it ſo vncertain, altering from tyme to time, not only at the pleaſure of the *Prince* that payeth, but alſo of the *Souldiours* that ſerue if they bee *Mercenarie*, that no

certaintie

certaintie can therein be wel fet downe. And very difficult it would be to determine any, that fhould not offend eyther the *Sculdiour* that ferueth, or the *Prince* that payeth.

The Paye alfo altereth, according to the *Conditions* of Entertaynment, for if the *Souldiour* bee allowed to Forrage *Gratis*, vpon the Countrie, as in thefe late Flemifh wars *Duke Caffimers* companies, & al other *Ruyters* did, then may their pay be the lefle.

But if there bee a *Forrage Maifter* that forrageth to to the vfe of the *Prince*, and ferueth the *Souldiours* by a price, then muft their pay be the greater, accordingly as the *Prince* meaneth to prize his *Forrage.&c.*

These circumftaunces confidered the *General* affembling his Counfell, may foone determine of the Rates & Payes to euery degree conuenient, which for diuerfe refpectes I thought not meete herevnto to be adioyned.

Of the General. Chap. 15.

General ought firſt in his owne perſon ſo to reforme all diſordered appetites, that his life maye ſerue as a mirrour to the whole Armie howe to reforme themſelues : for *Qualis Rex talis Grex*, And ſuch Example in the heade ſhal much more effectually work reformation in the whole bodye of the Soldiarie, then terror of Lawes, Neyther is there anye one thing that ſhall more traine Nations to his obedience, than the Fame of his Vertues and good life.

Aboue all things let him loue and feare God, and cauſe true Chriſtian Religion in his Armie to be had in due reuerence, in ſuch ſorte that his Souldiours may perceyue he is indeede Religious. And let him by al meanes cauſe the Miniſters of Gods word in his Armie to retayn their dignitie, and to be eſteemed and reuerenced of his Souldiours. For if the very Paynims by due obſeruation of their fayned Religion did kepe their Armies in maruellous obedience and order, how muche more ſhall true Religion deliuered from the Almightie Lorde of Hoſtes auayle a General and Armie that loueth him to the atchieuing of myraculous Victories.

He ought to be Modeſt, and Temperate, not giuen to Riote or exceſſe, neyther miſerablye bente to filthye Lucre : But preferre his honour, before all worldye ſubſtaunces No vain Vaunter, neyther to vendicate wholye to himſelfe the prayſe of good ſucceſſe, but to impute the ſame firſte to God, ſecondly to his Captaines and Souldiours that ſerue vnder him. And this Modeſtie, and Temperaunce, ſhall not only make his honourable Actions ſhine the more gloriouſlye, but alſo wonderfullye combine with harty good wyll his Souldiours to loue and honor him.

S. He

He ought to be a man of great Patience and Conftancie, in tolleration of labour and Mifaduenturs, nether difmapde with ill fucceffe noz puffed vppe wyth the contrarie, but hædefully to lay hold on al occafions, and carefully to profecute the good fucceffe, and pzeuent the contrarie, that neyther in Miferie be be founde Abiecte, noz in victozie Infolent.

Briefely, be muft be Religious, Temperate, Sober, Wife, Valiaunte, Liberal, Curtous, Eloquent, of good Fame and Reputation: learned in Hiftories, and in thofe Sciences and Artes that may enhable him of himfelfe, without directions from others, readily to conceyue and iudge of Militaire Actions of all foztes, wherein the Sciences Mathematical of all other foz this honourable perfon are moffe requifite to be embzaced.

A nobleman oz Gentleman trayned vp in thefe Sciences, and indued with thefe vertues, fhall farre fooner attayne to that perfection which in a General is needefull, than a perfon vnlearned. And moft Barbarous is the opinion of fuch as fuppofe Letters and Armes cannot wel ftande togither. Foz infinite are the Examples where Letters and Armes haue ioyned togither, euen in the moft famoufe and wozthy perfons of the wozld.

Was not Alexander the great trayned vppe in Philofophie vnder Ariftotle, and hadde the Illiades of Homer in fuche veneration, that he neuer trauelled oz refted without them.

Hannibal alfo that famous Enimy of the Romayne Empire, was trayned in the Greeke, the only learned language of that time, and lefte at his death a Booke of his owne making in the Greeke tongue. And when he pzepared to inuade *Italy*, of purpofe pzocured a learned *Grecian* to Leade, Guide, & Difcipline his Armie, by whofe lerned Counfels he vanquifhed fo many famous Romaine Confuls.

Alcibiades

Alcibiades a man of maruellous Prowesse among the *Grecians* , and so rare a Souldioure that Victorie did alwayes followe him what parte soeuer he did take, either wyth hys Countrey or agaynste it , was also trayned vppe in learnyng vnder that graue Philosopher *Socrates.*

Scipio Africanus the final Restoarer of the Romayne libertie, and subuerter of the Carthaginians , who gaue the notable ouerthrowe to that famous Hannibal, was likewise Learned, and did no lesse esteeme of Xenophnns booke of Cyrus, than the great Alexander of Homers Illiades.

Iulius Cæsar the firste founder of the Romaine Empire, and one of the moste renoumed Souldiours that euer the Earth Bare, was also singularly Learned, as appeareth by his conference with the Egyptian Philosophers aboute the Theoricke of the Sunne , and rectifying of the yearelye Reuolution, wherein, as among Souldiours for his Prowesse, so among Mathematitians for his Science he is registred, and to this daye those Solare Reuolutions or reformed yeares doe beare his name , and are among the Astronomers called *Anni Iuliani.* But if no other Testimonie of hys learnyng remayned, his owne Commentaries sufficientlye argue howe learned a man he was, whyche worke perhappes hath made hym no lesse famous, than al other hys honorable Actions.

I omit Epaminondas, Agesilaus, Fabius Maximus, Augustus Cæsar, Themistocles , and Silla, all famous Generals, and men excellently Learned. For infinite are the Examples, I mighte alleage to proue this Argument , but in a matter manifest it were baine to produce more witnesses. And this by experience I finde, þ it is only the grosse, ignoraunte, and ruder sort that hold this Opinion. For the moste Famous Souldiours this day in Christendom I know are of

another

another minde, and doe chiefelye efféeme of learning and of learned men.

And God sparing life I doubt not to make it apparaunte to my Countrey men, as well in the Art of Fortification, as manedging of greate Artilerie, and sundry other principall poyntes of Souldiourie, that the Sciences Mathematical are most necessarie, and may not be missed in such a Noble mã or Gentleman, as will aspire indéede to the perfection of Souldiourie.

Experience also in a General for the learning of manye particularities is a thing very requisite: And yet in respecte of that whiche by Letters also, I mean Histories, and Sciences, may be attayned, there is no comparison . *Multo enim latiùs circumspicit Mẽtis quàm Corporis oculus:* And in one yere may a man by reading knowe more sundry sortes of Embattayling , Encamping, and Fortifying, more Stratagems and Pollicies by famous Generals put in execution, more good Ordinaunces, Lawes, and Discipline for kéeping Souldiers in Order and Obedience, more rare deuises of Engins, Mynes, and like Militaire Inuentions , than is possible for him to sée in an hundred yeares Experience. And more perfection for Millitare gouernemente shal an Alexander, an Hanibal, a Scipio, or a Cæsar, trayned in learning, in two yeares Experience attayne. than some ignoraunt vnlearned person in twentie.

Hereof it commeth to passe that some one albeit he be a person of bodie strong, lustie, and couragious, hauing bene twentie yeares in the Warres , shall haue little more in him than to discharge the dutie of a Priuate Souldiour. And some other shall be by Nature of that Spirite and lyfe, and by learning of that Capacitie and Dexteritie , that wyth a fewe yeares Experience shal be worthie to be a Councellour to euery famous Generall. But *Dignior est qui pollet vtroq,*

And

And therefore an honourable perſon, meaning to become a perſite Souldiour, after he hathe by Science enriched hys mind and vnderſtanding, to ſatiſſie alſo common Opinion, I would haue him by vſe, practiſe, and experience, enfourme his ſenſes, and enable his bodie. And this cauſed the Antiquitie to portray the Statues of their Emperoures with a Booke in one hand, and a Sword in the other.

Emperours portrayed with a Booke in ane hād, and a Sword in the other.

If Kings and Princes in this ſort, for knowledge, Vertue, & Valure, would make choyſe of their Generals, they ſhould not nẽde to reſtreyne them within ſo narrow boundes by their Commiſſions, but leaue the manedging of the warres with more libertie to their Diſcretion, who fronting the Enimie, and being alwayes in the fielde preſente, ſhall euermore be able to make farre better Reſolutions, than the graueſt Senate, or Counſell of the worlde abſent, eſpecially in theſe Militare ſeruices, where many times Suddaine Reſolutions are required, and no time for Deliberation admitted, ſeeing ſuch Occaſions ſuddaynely maye be offered, as if preſently they be not accepted and purſued, in vayne afterward ſhall they be expected.

Firſt therefore, before the Generall receyue his Patent, it ſhall be requiſite for him to vſe the Counſell and aduiſe o certayne choyſe men, with whome he may conferre of al circumſtances concerning the Seruice, wherein he ſhall be employed, and ſo accordinglye make meanes to haue hys Commiſſion framed or amplified, and eſpecially to regarde that he haue as well allowance to rewarde the Vertuous and Valiant, as Authoritie to puniſhe the vitious and cowardly perſons. For that Generall that is readie to correct the Offender, and not reward the wel deſeruer, diſchargeth but the moytie of his Office.

Alſo, that immediately vpon the receyte of his Letters Patents, he haue due regard, that al his Officers, Colonels, and Captaynes, be men able to diſcharge their place & calling of themſelues, and not ſuche as ſometimes are choſen

by

by Fauour without Vertue, who being assigned to directe others, had more néede to séeke some other to directe themselues. For héerein chiefely consisteth the Valour and Wisedome of the Generall, to be able by conference to make due examination of mens habilities, and accozding to their Capacitie and Vertue, to committe charge vnto them : for that Generall that iudgeth onely by apparance and repozt, shall be extreamely abused, séeing it falleth often out, that men of great Fame by due triall are found of small sufficiencie.

It is also the Office of the Generall, not onely to sée that hys Coronels, and chiefe Officers haue their Pay and Furniture, but also that they impart the same duelie with theyz Souldioures. And if one quarter of the pay were committed to the custodie of their Ensignebearers, neuer to be answeered the Souldyers till the ende of the Warres, it woulde wozke many good effects.

The Generall ought not only to sée good chopse made of the Marshall, the Lieutenant of the Horsemen, the Treasourer, the Maysfer of the Ordinance, the Serieant Generall, the Scoutemaysfter, the Maysfer of ÿ Carriadges, of the Victualers, Miners, and Pioners, &c. but also to reuiew the election of euerie of his Captaynes and their Officers, to allow oz alter as he shall sée cause.

Also, if there happen to be vnder his charge moze Nations than one, it shall be requisite (to auoyd Enuie and contehtion) that he elect certayne chopse men of euery Nation, to be of his Counsell, with whome he should debate of euerie Enterpzise, & beare their Opiniós at large, but his Resolution shoulde be so secret, as none oz verie fewe shoulde hée made partakers thereof, befoze the execution.

The place of Assemblie where the Armie shoulde first Muster, should be appoynted in some holesome seate of some fertile Countrey, that at the beginning the Souldyoures bée not discouraged neyther by Sicknesse noz Penurie, murie.

Heere ought also the Generall to fée and examine euerie Officer, whether they haue a sufficient Proportion of Armour, Weapon, Shot, Powder, Artillerie, Boates to make Bridges to passe Riuers, Spades, and Mattockes, and euerie other particularitie, before they once begin to martch forward.

Heere ought also the Generall to assemble his Counsell, and to ordeyne Statutes and Lawes for the gouernement of hys Souldiarie, first communicating the same with his Coronels and Captaynes, causing them also to imparte them to their Bandes, suffering euerie man franckly with due reuerence, to speake, obiect, and by writing if they list, to offer vnto any of the Counsell what they can againste anye of them, which Obiections considered, they shal resolue vppon those Lawes and Penalties, and then cause euerie Coronell and Captaine to take his Oth, and they likewise to cause euerie Souldioure at the Ensigne to take their othes, to obserue, and as mutche as in them shall lie, to cause to be obserued euerie of these Lawes and Edicts so agréed on. Thys done, the Armie maye beginne to martch, whensoeuer the Generall séeth occasion.

The Generall is by good, especial, and perfite Plattes, Mappes, and Models, to know the Scituation, Nature, and propertie of the Countrey, and his parts, where he is to passe with his Armie, whether it be playne and Champion, or woodie, and full of waters, furnished wyth strong Townes, or contrarie, according to proportion the Horsemen and Footemen of his Armie: for if it be moste parte Champion, and full of Forradge, it is méete to haue the more Horsemen, if contrariwise, it standeth vpon straytes, and Fortified places, he is to haue the more Footemen.

Light Horsemen are in all places for Discouerie, fetching in of Booties, and pursuing of Victorie, verie seruiceable, and by no meaues to be spared.

The

The Generall ought also by good especiall to learne how his Enimie is appoynted: for againste the Frenche, who abound with Shotte, and haue fewe Pikes, the Launce and light Horsemans staffe of the North is singular good, and especially in the playne: But againste the Switzers and Lance-kneyghtes the Launce auaileth little, but the Pistoleters and Argoletiers shall muche more annoy them.

I like well to haue some Carriadges allowed in pay, to attende on euerie Bande of Footemen, as well as on the Horsemen, who besydes the Carriadge of necessaries for the Souldyers vse, maye also in tyme of Skirmishe, and other encounters, serue to carrie hurte men out of the fielde.

The Generall maye allow euerie Coronell, Captayne, and principall Officers in the fielde, certayne Gentlemen extraordinarie, whiche shall be selecte persons, able to discharge euerie Office vnder them, and also to supplie theyr places in euerie suddayne, and for suche to haue good paye and allowance, but for Dead payes I hold them not conueniente.

The Generall ought also not onely to haue expert Enginers, and menne of excellente knowledge in the arte of Fortification both of Fortes and Campes, conducting of Mines, planting of Batteries, &c. but also to haue therein himselfe exquisite knowledge, otherwise shal he be misledde by fantasticall deuises of suche as professe and vaunte themselues of the knowledge they are nothyng giltie, and purchase hymselfe perpetuall Dishonoure. And howe muche suche a Generall shall surmounte other, maye appeare by the Prince of Orange, who by reason of hys owne excellente knowledge in Fortification, hathe himselfe bin the chiefe or onely Enginer to make so many inuincible Cities and Townes, as in *Holland, Zeland, Brabant,* and *Flaunders* are at this day to be sêene: And thereby onely or chiefly of any humane cause, hathe bêene able to
make

The Arte of Fortification, a Study for a Generall.

The Prince of Orange.

make hed againste the most famous Souldiozs, and Generals of Christendome: And reduced the Country from moste
abiect Fortune to the state we may presently sée, contrary to
all expectation.

A Generall ought to haue good consideration of the place
where he meaneth to Encamp and continue, that it be not in
an vnholesome and infectious aire, but that his Souldioures
may lie on drie ground, and yet not farre distant from Wood
and Water, the which are so necessarie as in a Campe maye
not be spared: And if he perceiue Sicknesse in his Cápe to increase, the beste Remedy is often to remoue, and to encamp
vpon Hils and dry grounds, and to giue straite order that al
garbage of Beastes and other filth be enterred, & the Camp
preserued as swéete as possible maye be.

He is to giue order that his Souldiozs be kepte in Exercise, eyther in marching and trayning, oz in some kinde of
Militaire Labour, which shal not only enable their bodies in
strength and agilitie, but also preserue them in Health.

He shoulde while faire weather is, acquainte his Souldiozs to reste and sléepe on bare grounde: And though the Enimie be farre absente, yet duely to maintaine their Scoutes
to Watche and Warde, and perfozme all other Militaire orders no lesse curiously than if the Enimie were still present,
whereby it shall not séeme gréuous when necessitie shal re-
quyze it.

He is also befoze he Encamp to consider, if he haue abundaunce of Horse, that there be good stoze of Forradge nighe
the Camp, otherwise, in fozraging farre off, he may greatly
hazard his Companies, if good Conueys be not sent with his
Fozragers, and their iourneys discréetly directed.

Good regarde muste also be had, that the Campe be not
subiect to any Hil, from whence the Enimie may beate with
great Artillerie, noz so distoyned from Water, that the Enimie may easily cut you from it, neither yet so lowe as the
Enimie by cutting the bankes of any Riuer may drowne the
T. Camp.

Campe.

If there be no great Riuers, but onely ſmall Fountaines oꝛ Welles to water your Armie, then muſte good Watch be kept, that they be not by the Enimie poyſoned and infected.

The Generall ſhoulde not ſo mutche ſéeke to place hys Campe in ſeates ſtrong by Nature, as to Fortifie them by Arte, aſwell to kéepe hys Souldieures in Action, and from ydleneſſe,(the only ruine of Armies)as alſo that due oꝛder in Campes may be maintayned: And therefoꝛe let him imitate the auntient Romanes,the very Maſters of the Art of War, who neuer coueted other than the Plaine to encampe vpon: Entrenching themſelues nightly in no leſſe ſtrong and ſure maner,than if the Enimie had encamped by them, and that euen in places vtterly voide of all ſuſpition, to make theſe Militaire Trauelles familiar to them, and to auoide thoſe idle, oꝛ rather diſſolute Effeminate Paſtimes that oure Chriſtian Campes are bewitched with all,to the vtter ruine of all good Militaire Diſcipline, and confuſion of oure Armies.

Metellus in Affrike.

The Generall oughte foꝛ auoyding of Mutinies and all diſoꝛders within his Campe,to haue his Statutes and Lawes openly Proclaymed and ſet vp publikely foꝛ euerye man to reade,with the paine to euery offence aſſigned, and the ſame ſeuerely to be put in execution on all offendoꝛs without any reſpect of Perſons.

In a running oꝛ moueable Campe the readieſt Fortification is to impale it rounde with the Carriages chayned togither, bending the Artillerie that waye where moſte ſuſpition is the Enimie ſhall appꝛoche, and if tyme will permitte to caſte ſome Trenche alſo wythoute the Carriages.

The olde Engliſhe Encamping.

This Pollicie vſed the Duke of *Alba* in the late Flemiſh Warres, againſt the Prince of *Orange*, who inuading wyth a greate power of Horſe, and finding the Duke of *Alba* al moſte

Duke of Alba.

moste all Footemen impaled wyth Carriages, was neuer able to gyue him Battayle : And in the ende for wante of Forrage and Victualles was driuen to retyre.

He shoulde sée his Souldioures kepte in continuall Militaire Exercise, and by fayned Alarmes to sée in what readinesse his Bandes woulde be if necessitie requyred: To shewe them all manner wayes howe the Enimie maye attempte them, discouering also to them the remedye, and howe they are to aunswere those Attempts : For no manne is borne a *A man borne a Souldior.* Souldiour, but by Exercise and Trayning it is attayned : and by discontinuance againe it is lost, as all other Artes and Sciences. Neyther is there anye Nation for Militaire Actions so Honourable, as by Reste and Discontinuaunce *No Nation by nature alway Militare.* will not growe Effeminate and Reprochfull : For anye Nation by nature so abiect and base, that by a worthy Ge-*Rest Effeminates* nerall with Trayning will not produce good Souldiarie : *Trayning makes Souldiours.* As by infinite examples of Antiquitie maye bée approued. And in these dayes wée haue séene the Flemings, a people, by reason of theyr Reste, Riches, and Delicate Life, contemned, and no valure for Armes supposed in them : Yet *The Prince of Orange.* since the Prince of *Orange* hath put weapon into their hảds, and trayned them, they haue not onely defended themselues, but also in sundry exploites giuen the famous Spaniardes greate foyles : Suche is the valor of a graue wise General, as is able to chaunge the Nature and Fortune of an whole Nation *Annuente Deo.*

In setling of a Camp, besides the commodities of Wood, Water, and Forrage, the Generall muste also consider how Victualles may safely come vnto him: And to leaue no Castelles at his backe to annoy them, but that hée séeke to possesse them before he martche forwarde : For greate is the annoyaunce that a little Pile at the backe of an Armie may do, aswel against Forragers and Straglers, as to cutte off Victuallers from the Campe.

The Generall is also by good Plattes to consider the

T.ij.   Scituation

Scituation of the Countrey, howe, bothe the Friend and Enimie Townes lye from his Campe, the Hilles and Valleys, Ways, Straits, and Passages, Lakes, Riuers, and Bridges, their number, quantitie, distance, and euerye particularitie, which maye be done by conference with his Guydes, and other persons that knowe the Countrie, conferring their assertions with his Plattes: And so to consider, whether the Enimie maye conueniently sende out to cutte off his Victuallers, or by Ambush annoy him in his Marche, and for preuention thereof to sende abroade both Light Horsemen and Harquebuziers to garde the straites and passages, towards the Enimies Garnisons. Herein is Iulius Cæsar singularly

Iulius Cæsar. extolled by Suetonius Tranquillus to surmount all other for chosing his grounde to Marche, Encampe, and Fight vpon: Wherein by the singular knowledge he had, bothe in Geographie and Astronomie, he woulde prudently forecaste all annoyaunces of Sunne, Winde, and Weather: The nature and Scituation of the Countrie, of Riuers, Hilles, Valleys, Woodes, Straites, and such like, by Geographicall Cartes and Mappes exactly made. And hereby also hath the Prince

The Prince of Orenge. of Orenge in these late Flemishe warres greatly aided himselfe: For hauyng of Hollande, Zelande, and all other partes of the lowe Countries verie perfite and exquisite Mappes &

Geographie for a Souldior requisite. Plattes, he was able at one time in sundrie partes to giue Direction whiche Straites shoulde be garded, what places Fortified, whiche Leuels might be Drowned either by Sea, or fresh waters. And thereby often auoided present and impendent perilles, and contrarie to all expectation, hath roosted out the Spanishe Enimie of so manye strong Fortes and Townes by them possessed.

Before the Armie discampe, al Passages and Wayes for the Souldiors and Artillerie &c. to passe, should be discouered, and skilfull men appointed to leade them, whiche of the Romanes were named Campiductores.

He ought not to suffer any Band to martche scattered, but

but in order of Battell, or at leaste if Straites and narrowe Passages inforce to draw them forth in Herses, and presently so soone as place serueth to reduce them againe into order of Battel: And this is to be vsed as wel in places of Securitie, for Exercise and Reputation, as in places of Suspecte for safetie and Defence.

He oughte to haue wyth him good Guides that perfitely knowe all particular Passages, Hilles, Valleys, Woodes, Riuers, &c. for of the Countrey in generalitie the Generall himselfe ought perfitely to be informed by Plattes and Modelles, whereby also he shall the more readily conceiue any information that shall be brought him by espiall.

If the Generall haue sundrie Nations vnder his gouernement, it is not méete to giue alwayes to anye one Nation the Vaward, considering (the same being in marching towardes the enimie the place of greatest honour) the others wil much repine against it, and not without good cause. The order therefore of Marching shoulde in such sort be framed, that euery Nation shoulde haue his turne withoute partiall fauoure to any one. And if the number be great of anye one Mercinarie Nation, it is not amisse to deuide them bothe in Marching and Imbatteling for sundrye respectes, whiche in this place I omitte to declare.

Obserued by Count Bossute, and Monsieur Lanovv in their Ordinances.1578. in Braband.

If any Straite be kepte by the Enimie, it is not méete first to charge thé vpon the very Front, but to send Light Horsmen and Shotte to skirmishe with them on either Flancke, and then wyth Targets of Proofe to enter vpon them.

The Generall shoulde before he bring hys Souldiors to deale with the Enimie, first in some plaine and Champion place cause them to be ranged in forme of Battell, makyng of his Footemen sundry Battallions: And of these Battallions sundry Frontes, to deuide hys Horsemen also into sundrye Troupes, placing the men at Armes, Dimilaunces, Lighte Horsemen, and Argoletiers euery sort in seuerall Troupes by themselues, to cause thb Forelorne Hope to issue oute

Pastimes for a Generall.

and skirmishe before the Battallions, as if the Enimie were indéede present, and vpon a Signe giuen, sodainely to retire. The Horsmen to charge and returne againe to their place, vpon their retire to cause certaine sléues of Pikes, and light armed, to runne out to their Rescue, as though the Enimie did pursue them. Then the Battallions of the firste Fronte to marche forwarde, and bende their Pikes, and so dainelye after sounde of the Retreite, to retire themselues orderly betwéene the Battallions of the second Front: Then that seconde Front to martch forward and bend their Pikes, and the other that firste retyred to make hed againe vppon the Enimie. Last of all, the Light Horsemen, and Light Armed Footemen againe to breake forth as it were to doe execution vpon the Enimie Flying.

Triall of trayned Souldiors.

These thinges, if in pastime they be able readily and orderly to performe, there is good hope they will honorablye put it in execution vpon the Enimie : Otherwise to bring them without this former Trayning to deale with the Enimie, is nothing else but to leaue them to the Butcherie.

It is aboue all other things for a Generall requisite by al meanes to animate his Souldiors to Frugalitie in expences, and Tolleration of Labour: For it is not the wilde, rashe, fantasticall heade, but the sober obedient minde, and the harde painfull bodie that maketh the Noble Souldior. And nothing more continueth the Bodie in Health and Strégth than Exercise. Sundry sortes therefore of Militaire Actiuities an Traynings the Generall shoulde deuise, and enioyne his Coronelles and Captaines to kéepe their Souldioures in continuall Actions, for the Body of man is in qualitie like yron.

What Natures proue Souldiors.

Pulchrum est vsu cessans, rubigine sordet.

Let the Generall consider the nature of the Enimie, Nations with whom he dealeth : If they be of Delicate Bodies, not hardned in War: Or if he perceiue that Victualles fayle them,

them, Or that ſickneſſe encreaſe among them : Let hym in any wiſe abſtaine from Battell , for more aſſuredlye ſhall hée that waye preuaile. And as honourable doe I iudge the Victorie to the Generall, by that Pollicie attayned, as if by the bloude of his Souldiours he ſhoulde atchieue it.

There is nothing more perillous in giuing Battell, than to laye before the Souldioures eyes any place of Refuge to fly vnto: But rather ſhould the Generall declare vnto them, that there is no hope to eſcape, but onely by Victorie , and herein to imitate the proceeding of Hanniball againſte the Romanes.

There is nothing more Barbarous than in giuing Battel to committe all to the hazarde of one Fortune or Encounter. But in ſuche ſorte deuide the Regiments , that if one be defeated, there maye remayne others in order to charge vpon the Enimie, who following Victorie with diſorder, as commonly it is ſéene : If they were but the thirde parte of theyr enimies number, yet may they recouer the field againe. And in this to imitate the Romane Diſcipline, who euer ſo ranged their Armies, that Fortune muſte at the leaſte thrice abandon them, and fauour thrice their aduerſaries, or elſe they coulde not be vanquiſhed.

There is nothing more perillous than to giue the Enimie Battell in ſuche place where he hath no Refuge or Poſſibilitie to eſcape , for that Neceſsitie maketh men Deſperate, it vniteth them togither : And it hathe often béene ſéene, that verye ſmall companies by ſuch like occaſions being reduced to Deſperation, therevpon reſoluing to ſell their liues déerely , haue contrary to all expectation attayned Victorie vppon their Enimies in number farre greater.

In this caſe did 6000. Engliſh defeate 60000. French at Poicti- ers.

Coronelles, Captaines, and ſuche principall perſons aughte not to bée thruſte in Rancke as Priuate Souldioures,

ours, but being at libertie, muche moze oughte they by Hed and Tongue to direct, than with Hande to execute, albeit sometimes in cases of Extremitie they are to execute with the Hande also, but in day of Battell to put al the pzincipall Officers into the first Rankes, where they can doe no moze than Priuat Souldiors, it is Barbarous, and by an Honozable wise Generall by no meanes to be permitted.

Footemen lightly armed, bothe Pikes and shozt weapon, as Swozdes and Targettes to mire with Shot, are of great seruice. Uery famous Generalles, finding themselues ouer matched by Horse (their Enimie in Cauallarie far surmounting them) haue in the day of Battaile giuen ozder, that certaine Troupes of these light armed shoulde assist their own Hozsemen : and after the Charge was by them receiued, these Light Armed should with a Cry in great furie bzeake vpon the Enimies Troupes of Hozse : And haue by that meane not onely rescued their owne, but also so bzoken and chaced the enimie Cauallarie, that contrary to all expectation, thereby onely they haue defeated them, and wonne the fielde : A Pollicie to be reuiued where the Generall shal find himselfe in Cauallarie too weake.

Cæsar againste Pompey.

Scanderberg against the greate Turke.

These light armed Footmen should be trained of purpose to fight among Horsemen, to followe the Enimie in Chace, and yet vpon any sodaine to vnite themselues againe in one Bodie, to abide a Charge, and sodainly againe to bzeake and followe the Chace, and oftentimes to reiterate the same, to put the like in execution againste the Enimie when occasion is offered, whiche by Practise right well will be attayned, howe strange soeuer nowe foz wante of vse in these dayes it may seeme vnto vs.

The Romanes vsed a kinde of Forelorne Hope oz Skirmishers called *Cursores* oz *Proclastas*, whiche they diuided into thzee sortes, *Antistites*, *Cornistites* and *Tergistites*, neyther woulde they euer tourne out any of these to skirmishe, but that they were backed with Armed men, Pikes, Swozdes,

Reuiued by the Spaniardes.

and

and Targets, or suche like : And these they called *Vindices*, Reuengers or Rescuers : And this shoulde also euen in these dayes with our Shot be practised, as well to garde thē from the Charge of Horse, as to aide them if they shoulde ioyne pele mele with their Enimies: As the Spaniards haue of late dayes begonne to practise.

Skirmishes shoulde neuer rashly be made nor vsed at any time, but to some ende and purpose, as to Discouer, or win some grounde of Aduauntage, or some Straite, or before the Battell to giue Souldiors Courage, by giuing the Enimie some Foile: but the leading of suche a Skirmishe, oughte to be committed to some sober, wise, discreete, valiaunt Gentleman, who either by laying secreate Ambushes and Receites, or by some other Traine and Pollicie may be assured to giue the Enimie some Foile. For that kinde of Fleshing the Souldiors before the Battell, is a matter of greate importaunce, not onely to them that were present at the Skirmishe, but also to the whole Armie, who by their example wil take Courage and Boldnesse. And as a Generall ought by al meanes to seeke this aduantage, so oughte he to be as warie that his Enimie get not the like vpon him, and to preuent the same, must giue commaundement, that no man vpon pain of Death be so hardie as to enter in Skirmish wyth the Enimie, without expresse commaundement from hymselfe or some of his principall Officers.

Skirmishes to vvhat ende.

As a Generall ought neuer giue battayle to his Enimie, wythout great and apparant reason either of Aduauntage or Necessitie, so is he chiefly to abstaine if he perceiue hys Souldiors to haue conceiued any secreate feare. And herein greatly auaileth the wisedome of the General, to discern the nature and disposition of his Souldiors, and by comfortable and couragious wordes to animate them, and (as hath bin saide) by Skirmishes of aduantage to Fleshe them, and by continuall Trayning to make them knowe their strength and aduauntage of their Orders and Discipline:

Note Iulius Cæsar after his battel at Durazzo.

U.   And

And by no means to giue entire Battel, til he haue by some of these or like meanes banished all feare from them. For there is no Enimie sooner ouerthrown, than he that wil accept Battell whensoeuer it is offered, as by manye Presidents may playnely be approued.

If in the Winter time the Enimie present Battell early in the morning, our Generall by Skirmishes shoulde delay and prolong the time as long as he maye: and in the meane tyme cause all his Souldiors, especially the heauie armed, to fæde and refreshe themselues with meate & Drinke, and then bring them to deale with ẙ Enimie, whom if they find with colde and fasting weakned, there is greate likelihœde of gœd Successe. By this mean only was there one greate Army of the Romanes at ẙ riuer of *Trebes* vtterly ouerthrowen, by reason their Generall being ouermuche desirous to giue Battell, brought forth his Armie to fight, not suffering them to stay the fæding and refreshing of themselues before hande.

It were conuenient to appointe certaine Carriages and men, of purpose to giue their attendance in euery skirmishe and incounter, to carry away the hurt men to such place as Surgions may immediately repayre vnto them, whiche shal not only greatly incourage the Souldior, but also cause the Skirmish to be the better mainteined, when the Souldiors shal not nœde to leaue the fielde to carry away their hurte men. These were called among the Romanes *Despotati.*

Reuiued by the
Spaniardes.

And this amõg many other laudable Romane Orders haue the Spaniards at this day reuiued and put in practise, wherby also they conceale from their Enimie what losses in any Skirmishe they haue receiued, a matter of no small importaunce.

Hannibal that famous Generall, woulde seldome or neuer giue Battel, but he had before hand inuented some Pollicie to giue terror to his Enimies, by some sodain attempt of secrete Ambushments, either on their Flācke or Backe,

accom-

accommodating his deuice to the oportunitie of the time &
place, which in his laſt Battel with Scipio he coulde not ſo
wel do, by reaſon the place was plaine & Champion, where
onely Magnanimitie and good Diſcipline mighte preuaile:
wherein the Romanes being nothing inferiour, he had not
that fortunate ſucceſſe, which in many other battels he had
againſt them. A worthy Generall therfore ſhoulde borowe
bothe of Hannibal his ſubtile Stratagemes: And of the Romanes their Warlike Orders and Diſcipline: And in execution of ſuch Pollicies, Secrecie is aboue al other things to
be reſpected: for as there is no Stratageme ſo excellēt, which
being knowne the Enimie may not preuente, ſo is there almoſt no deuice ſo ſimple, ẏ being ſecreatly kept, and ſodain-
ly putte in execution, but it will worke ſingular good effectes.

Hannibal and Cæſar Patternes for a Generall.

To the Generall of the fielde it appertaineth, al the time
of the Battel to giue order, when the ſkirmiſhers, or Forelorne Hope ſhall retyre, and to what places: When the
Horſemen ſhall charge, what Troupes either of Horſmen
or light armed Footemen ſhal come to their Reſcue: What
Battallions ſhall martche forward, when they ſhall retyre,
when the light armed ſhall purſue the Victorie. For thys
and all other accidents that may happen during the time of
Battell, the General ought attentiuely to giue order from
time to time what ſhall be done: And that aſwel by Meſſen-
gers which ſhal alwayes attende vpon his perſon for that
purpoſe, as by the ſoundes of the Trumpette and Drummes.

The Generall in the day of Battayle.

And albeit ſundry be the Opiniōs of Souldiors touching
the Place of the General in the day of Battel: Some would
haue him mounted on Horſebacke, others on Foote: Some
in the hearte of ſome Squadron or Battallion neare the
Enſigne or Standarde: Others at libertie not tyed to
to any place certain. And for confirmatiō of euerie of theſe
Opinions, the Examples of very worthy Generalles maye
be

be alleaged. Yet briefly to set downe vpon consideration of sundry Discourses that I haue heard & read, what I thinke best, I say, I would not haue the General mounted on any principall Horse of Seruice, but vpon some Nag, (I meane such a General as is strong in Footmen) neither to put himselfe into any Battallion or Squadron, but being accompanied with a reasonable strong Guard, and certaine very sufficient Gentlemen likewise mounted vppon Nags, to passe from place to place, from one Battallion to an other, during the time of Battel, prescribing continually what he woulde **The Place and** haue done, sending of these Gentlemen to deliuer his mea-**Duety of the Ge**ning and commaundementes to suche Officers as are to see **nerall in the day** them presently put in execution. And neuer to put himselfe **of Battel.** into the bodie of any Battallion or Squadron, vnlesse he see the Enimie so preuaile, that his Skirmishers and light armed be beaten in, the Battallions of his former Frontes retired, and that the matter is reduced euen to the laste fight: Then may the General either dismount, & enter into some select Battallion to make the laste trial, or into some principall Squadron of Horse, to giue order for the retyre of his people, and safegard of his person, if he see no other remedy.

The Romanes If the Enimie haue newe aide, and supply of menne com-**against** *Hannibal* ming vnto him, then oughte the Generall to seeke al means **and** *Asdrubal.* to giue him battel, before both his powers ioyne: Or if Victualles and Pay beginne to faile vs, or be likely to growe dayly more scarce among vs, oure Generall shoulde neuer refuse Battel, if any oportunitie be offered: But otherwise, if our General expect further supply, or y̌ oure enimies Victuals fayle them, or Sicknesse increase among the, let him stand strongly vpon his Guard, but by no means ioine battell with them so long as he can conueniently auoide it.

The Experiēce hereof was lately seene in these Flemish Warres. 1578. betwéen the States and Don Iohn *D'Austria,* **Don Iohn** and who vnderstāding of the cōming of Duke Casimere with **Counte** *Bossute* at 5000. Ruiters, and 6000. Footemen, offered the Armie of **Rymenant.** the

the States battayle at *Rymenant*, where they laye encamped to expect Duke Casimers comming. But Counte Boslute Generall of the States Armie, albeit bothe for Footmen and Horsemen he was well able to haue foughte wyth hym, yet gaue he straighte order, that none of hys armed should stirre out of the Trenches, but onlythe Shot, and certaine Horse to guarde Passages, and maintaine Skirmishe, so that Don Iohn finding his expectation deceiued, and that he coulde not traine them forthe to the Battaile, was dri uen to martch away. And this Temperaunce in the Count Boslute was no lesse Sodiarelike, than the other couragi ous attempt of Don Iohn, both being done w great reason.

If at any time, by reason the General perceiueth his ad uersary ouer strong, he thinke good to martch away to pla ces of more strength, he shoulde so vse the matter, that hys Souldiors by no means vnderstande or suspecte it is done to auoide Battell, but rather to signifie vnto them his in tention is to retyre, to the ende he may drawe the Enimie vpon his Ambushes, or into some groundes where he maye giue them Battell to his better Aduantage, for otherwise the Retire may strike so great a Terrour into the heartes of his Souldiors, as hardly after will be remedyed by anye perswasions.

If the Enimie vpon our retreite pursue vs, the Generall musse giue order to lay sundry Ambushments of Shotte to guarde Straites and Passages, & also to leaue certain Troups of light Horse and others by skirmish to stay them, while ŷ heauie armed may marche awaye. But if the Enimie pur sue vs so faste, that our armed Fanterie cannot march away in Militaire order, let the Generall prepare to giue them battel, and rather choose to put it to that honourable triall, than in any iote to breake his Militaire orders, or by disor dered Martch to strike a fear in ŷ hearts of his Souldiors.

Before the Battel, the Generall musse giue commaunde mente vpon paine of Death, that no Victualler, or other

Attilius a Romane Consul. Philip King of Macedony against the Scythians.

person whatsoeuer shal departe away, during the fight. And some famous Generalles haue appointed certayne Troups of Horse of purpose to attend and do execution on any such as they shoulde perceiue to breake or offer to escape away.

Hannibal against the Romanes in the Battayle of Cannas. Marius againste the Cymbri.

It is no small aide in the day of Battel to get the Sunne, the Wind, and the higher grounde of the Enimie, for these being on our side, and againste our Enimie, they fighte for vs, and albeit they séeme matters of small importance, yet the wisest and valiauntest Captaines haue not a little respected them.

Some haue in the day of Battell caused certaine of their owne Bandes, to reuolte to their Enimie, who afterwards haue bin no small cause of their Victorie. As Hanniball against the Romanes in the battel of *Cannas*.

Muscleborough Fielde.

Some in the time of Battel by corrupted espies or otherwise haue caused rumour to be spread in the Enimies Battell, that their Generall was slayne, or some part of them defeated, or flying awaye, and thereby so amazed them in the middest of the fighte, that they haue swayed and bro

T. Quintius Capitolinus.

ken : But thys muste be done on the contrarye parte of the Battayle, where the Generall is not to bée séene.

Some haue caused certaine of theyr owne Troupes euen vpon the first encounter to breake and runne awaye of purpose, to the ende the Ennimie mighte followe the chace vppon them wyth disorder, and so fall into the handes of the other Troupes standing orderly to receiue them.

Iulius Casar in Fraunce.

Some hauing enuironed their Ennimies rounde aboute, and perceyuing that the same hath made them more desperately to fighte, and resolutely to stande to their Defence, haue of purpose opened and made a way for their Enimies to flye : And by that Pollicie onely haue had the chace and slaughter of them , that otherwise woulde dearely haue

solde

folde they; lyues, o; perhappes haue gotte the Victorie.
As a small Troupe of oure Countreymen didde vppon the
Frenche in the like cafe at the Battell of Poyctiers, where
albeit they were not a tenth part of their enimies number,
yet being enuironed, hauing no place of Refuge, and there-
fo;e refolued dearelye and honourably to fell their Liues,
contrarye to all expectation they hadde Victorie, and
twke Iohn the French King Prifoner, with the flaughter of
a greate multitude of his Nobilitie.

Hannibal againft the Germanes.

Some fæyng they; Ennimie defirous to paffe a Ry-
uer, to gyue them Battayle, haue fæmed fo; feare
to martche awaye, leauing fecreate Ambufhes, and
when they haue percepued a good parte of the Armie paft
the Riuer, haue fodainely tourned agayne, and defeated
them befo;e the refidue were able to paffe ouer to they; ref-
cue.

Labienus in Fráce

Some abounding in Horfemen, to d;awe their Ennimie
into the Champion, haue offered Charges, and therevppon fayned a flyghte, thereby trayning the Enimie
into the Playne, where they haue defeated hym, whome in
Straites they were neuer able to encounter.

King Iu inba Affrike againft Curio.

Some leaders of Footemen haue alfo by fayning
flyght, trayned their Ennimie Cauallarie into Straites, and
there by fecrete Ambufhes fodainelye fette on them, and
defeated them, whome in the Champion they were not
able to deale wythall.

Thomiris Queene of Scithia againft Cyrus.200000. horfemen.

Some finding they; Souldiours ouermuche defirous to
fighte with the Ennimie, when it was not by due refpects
conuenient, and thereuppon repining againft the Generall
fo; kæping them from Battell, to make them knowe their
Error, hath of purpofe fuffered fome parte in attempting
fome rafhe enterp;ife to be defeated of the Ennimie, and
vppon that occafion made the refte vnderftand their
faulte, and become the mo;e obedient to his commaundements.

Fabius Maximus fo vfed Minutius And Sertorius likevvife vfed hys mutinous fouldioures.

Some

Hannibal.

Some haue of purpose abandoned their own Campe, as though they had fled fo2 feare, leauing it ful of wine and other Delicacies, and the night following, haue returned and set vpon those their enimies, who thinking themselues in Securitie, and d2owned in those Delicacies, haue béen rechlesse and vnp2ouided, and so by their Enimies when they leasse suspected, put to the Swo2de and vtterly defeated.

Q uintus Luttatius against the Cimbri.

Some being pursued of their Enimie, euen to a Riuer, whiche they must either passe, o2 receiue Battell, haue setled down at the riuer side, entrenching themselues, setting vp some Tents, & sending ab2oad some Foragers as though they meant indéede to encampe. And their Ennimies beléeuing the same, haue likewise encamped and sente ab2oade their people to make p2ouision: In the meane time those so pursued, vsing this occasion of their Ennimies negligence, and the aide of the night ensuing, haue sodainely passed the riuer befo2e the Enimie coulde dislodge and d2awe his people in o2der to giue them battell.

Nabides againste the Romanes.

Some being in like so2te pursued by a puissant Enimie, haue caste a Trench at their backe towards their Enimie, and filling the same with Woode and other matter fitte to burne, haue set it on fy2e, and so stayed the Furie of their Enimie till they haue passed ouer.

Some to passe a Riuer, otherwise not passable, haue lette it out by opening the Bankes into some lower grounde, but the best is in an Armie Royal neuer to be without Boates of purpose, that chayned togither, shall p2esentlye make a Bridge: Whereof in an other Treatise among other Militaire Engines I meane mo2e at large to speake.

Some being fronted by their Enimy on the contrary side of a Riuer, whereby they could not passe ouer to giue hym Battel without extreme disaduantage, after they had sund2y dayes togither marched along the Riuer, they that desired to passe, haue in the night out of euery Band d2awen a certaine number of choice men, whome they haue sente secretly cretely vnto the nexte Woodes, with direction, that the nexte day after the Armies were departed they ſhould come down to make and Fortifie their Bridge. The next day they haue both diſcamped, and their Enimie ſeeing the ful wonted number of Bandes, Enſignes, &c. haue withoute miſtruſte of anye ſuche matter marched on, fronting their Enimye as before they were accuſtomed. But thoſe that meant to paſſe, when they ſawe time, haue ſodainely returned backe again, and finding their bridge made, Fortified, & all things in readineſſe, haue paſſed withoute any daunger at all.

Some to paſſe a Riuer, though wadeable, yet verye violent and ſwift, haue cauſed their Horſemen, firſte in two places to paſſe and croſſe it, and then the Footmen to paſſe betwéene thoſe Troups of Horſe: the one Troup breaketh the force of the water, & if any of the footmen happé to faile his footing, & be borne away with the violéce of the ſtreame, yet the other Troupe of Horſe may recouer him. *Vigetius* Rule.

Some hauing ſundry Nations in their Armie, haue ranged euery Nation ſeparately into ſundrie Battallions, and haue put in the Forefronte a Battallion of euery Nation, giuing it oute in the time of fight, that one Nation had Victorie, wherewith the reſte inflamed ſhoulde likewiſe valiantly fighte: and by this Strategeme a wiſe Generall, ſhall greately aide himſelfe when he hath to commaunde ſundry Nations. *Monſieur Lautrek in the Kingdom of Naples.*

Some whé they haue perceyued theyr Enimies, by their labor and trauel, or haſtie purſute, to be wearie, or by long ſtanding in Battaile fainte, haue euen then vpon that occaſion ſodainely ſet on them, and defeated them, as oure Countrimen did the Frenche at the Battel of *Creſſie.* *Scipio againſte Aſdrubal. Metellus againſt Sertorius in Spaine.*

Some finding themſelues too weake in Horſemen, haue retyred themſelues among Vines, Buſhes and ſuche like vneuen groundes. Others haue made ſecrete Trenches, couering them with Hurdles, and Turffe: Others haue v- *The Spaniardes againſte the French at Cyrignola.*

æ.　　ſed

sed Caltrops and Stakes. By these and manye other meanes the ingenious Fanterie haue and euer will be Victorious against Cauallarie that rashly wil charge vpō them.

The Carthaginenses, who manye tymes hadde béene by Marcus Regulus ouerthrown, at the last by the counsell of Zātippus the Lacedemonian they became Victorious: who aduised thē to descend into the Plaines, where by their Elephants and multitude of Horse, they ouerthrewe the Romanes.

Some hauing with their Troupes of Launces sundrye times charged a Battallion of Pykes, and béene still repulsed with losse, at lasse haue caused all their Horsemen to Dismounte, and encountring on fœte, haue defeated the Battell of Pykes, whiche on Horsebacke they could not by any meane breake or disorder.

Some in the day of Battell perceiuing their Enimie to haue reduced his principal strength to some one part, haue not to the same opposed likewise their strongest Battallions, but their weakest, giuing order, that when they came almosse readie to encounter, they shoulde retyre, and suffer the resse to deale, and by that Pollicie firsse defeating the weaker, haue easily after dealte with the stronger, who being both inuironed of them, and also disordered, in pursuing those that of purpose haue retyred, were without any great difficultie afterwarde defeated.

Some haue drawne their Cauallarie, and light armed, behinde their Battallions of their heauie armed Souldiours, leauing betwéene those Battallions sufficient space for the Horse to Charge, and Shotte to Play, by whiche Noueltie, happening so contrarye to common order, and their Enimies expectations, they haue attayned Victorie:

Some haue broughte before the Front of their Enimies battell a number of Carriages drawen with Oxen, & laden with dry Wœdde and other stuffe fit to burne, and sodainely giuing fire vnto them, the Beastes to flye the flame at their

their fayles, haue violentlye runne forward, and broken
the arraye of the Ennimie. Others haue vsed Hooked
Wagons and other Engins, whiche of their owne Violence by secrete inward Motions do worke the like effects.

Some aswell to resiste these Engins, as also the charge
of Launces and Barbed Horses, haue caused euerie Souldiour of the firste Ranckes of their battell to haue Stakes
of foure or fiue foote in length, sharpe at bothe endes,
and those to thrust into the earth, bending them towards
the Ennimie, and to couer them with their bodies, til
they see the Enimie giue the charge, then presentlye to
retire, and receiue them vppon those ranckes of Stakes.

Sylla against Ar-
chelaus.

The Englishe
againste the
French at *Egin-*
court.

Some finding themselues too weake to giue their Ennimies Battell, haue entred into *Parle* of Peace, seeming as
though they were ready to yeelde to any Conditions, and
by that meane prolonged the time, till either they mighte
haue further supply from their friendes, or oportunitie to
marche secretly away.

Sylla in Cappado-
cia.

Some finding themselues too weake to giue their Enimies Battel, haue dispersed their Souldiors into sundrye
Townes, and Castels, Fortifying and Victualling those
their Holdes, and so by prolonging the Warres, consu-
med their enimies Treasure, and thereby dissolued the Armie, which otherwise they had neuer bin able to defeate.
Thys Pollicie is beste to be vsed when Winter draweth
on, whiche in these Northerne Countreys is a sufficient
Enimie to consume anye great Armie that shall then still
keepe the fielde.

The Prince of
Orange against
the Spaniardes
in the lovve
Countries.

Some hauing one of their Townes besieged, to giue
them a supply of Men and Victualles, haue with their Armie marched on, bruting by espiall, that they meante to
giue the Ennimie Battell, who presently hathe leuied hys
Siege, and marched on to meete hym, the rather to
auoyde Sallies oute of the Towne on their backe during the fighte: But so soone as by this policie they had

Fraunch the
Frenche King a-
gainst the Empe-
rour *Charles* the
fift at *Landersey.*

with-

withdzawne the Siege, and entred certaine Bandes with a pzopoztion of Victuals, secretely the next nighte they Discamped and marched awaye.

Some hauing summoned a Castell, strongly Scituate vpon an hil, enuironed with Marishe, in suche sozte, that it was thought impossible to bzing the Cannon to batter it, and therefoze the Captaine of the Castell, refusing to yéeld except he might sée the Cannon : The Generall wythoute, hath secretely caused a Cannon of Woodde to be artificially made and coloured, Hurdles to be laide vppon the Marish, a number of Hozseto dzawe the Carriages, as though with greate difficultie they had dzawn a Cannon indéede, and then thzeatning, that accozding to the Lawe of Armes they should be all put to the Swozd, if they did abide ý Batterie : The Captaine of the Castell abused by thys Stratageme, hath surrendzed the Forte by Composition, whiche otherwise hadde coste a number of mens liues befoze they shoulde haue gotten it.

Some determining to surpzize one strong Towne, haue firste offered to laye siege to some other thereby, suffering it notwithstanding to be supplyed from the other (whiche they meante indéede to besiege) with Victuals, Munition, and Souldiors : whyche done, they haue immediately bent their whole fozces vppon that Towne from whence these Supplies departed, and finding the same by thys Pollicie the moze dissurnished, haue in shozter tyme atchieued it.

Some knowing a Towne so strongly scituate, and well foztified, that by fozce of Batterie, Scale, oz Mine, they hadde no hope to gette it, haue onely wasted and spoyled the Countrey rounde aboute them, cutting off all supplye of Victualles from them, not suffering anye of the people to issue foozthe, and so in tyme by Famine onely infozced it to yéelde, whyche otherwise wythoute maruelous slaughters, and Butcherie of menne coulde neuer haue béene gayned.

The Lorde Pooninges at Saterdeboys in Fraunce.

King Henry the eight to vvinne Bulleine.

Môsieur Lautrech to vvinne Pauia in Italy.

The Prince of Orange to vvin Middleboroughe and diuers other strong Tovvns in Zeland and Holland.

Don Iohn de Austria to gette Philipville.

gayned.

Some by giftes and promises haue corrupted the chiefe Captaines, or set Dissention betwéene the Souldiours and Citizens: Or maintained some Faction before begonne among them And then by espiall hauing intelligence when matters were grown to ripenesse and perfection, giuing the one side secrete aide, vpon the sodaine haue surprised the other Faction, and wonne the Towne.

Casrucchio for the gayning of diuers States in Tuscane.

Some hauing a Towne of theirs besieged with suche an Armie as they were not able to leauie wyth anye power of theyr owne, haue by cutting open certayne Banckes, let in the Sea, in such abundaunce, that they haue drowned all the Countrey saue onely certaine Hilles and Banckes, whereuppon after their enimies were retired, with small flat botomed Boates for that purpose prepared, they haue victualled their friends besieged, and supplyed them with men and munition: And by that meanes saued and rescued the Townes, that otherwise of Necessitie must shortly haue bin losse.

The Prince of Orange for rescue of Tovvnes in Holland and Zeland.

Some hauing laide siege to a strong Town, vpon a Sallie made by the Citizens, haue fained flight, abandoning their Campe, suffering the besieged enimies to take a spoile thereof. But after they had allured by that pollicie greate numbers of the Souldiours and Citizens to this spoile, they haue from secreate Ambushes sette vpon these Citizens thus laden with Spoiles, and pursuing the slaughter of them, (euen to the Walles and Gates of the Towne) haue entred pele mele with them, and by that pollicie possessed the Citie.

A Pollicie put in execution by Hannibal.

Some hauing a Breache made in the Curtaine of theyr Towne or Bulwarke, haue inwardly made certaine Countertrenches and secrete Mines, laying in them Barrells of Powder, and other murthering Fireballes, and vpon the assault giuen, haue retyred themselues, suffring their Enimies in great numbers to enter, maintayning their inward

Counte Pietro Nauarese in Italy did by these meanes many notable seruices

Practised also in thys laste siege of Maestricht.

Æ.iij.   Tren-

Trenches, till suche time as they did sée Oportunitie, and then giuing fire to their secrete Mines, haue made so great a slaughter of their enimies, that folowing the same confusion and disorder with a couragious Sallie, they mighte haue leuied the siege.

Some séeing theyr Towne no longer possible to be defended, haue in the night set fire thereon, and made a Sallie oute, on that parte where they perceiued the Siege weakest, & by that means haue saued a great parte of their people, not without the slaughter of many of theyr Enimies.

Mythridates pursued by Lucullus. And Tryphon King of Syria solovved by Antiochus.

Some being by theyr Ennimies pursued, haue lefte dispersed behinde them Treasure here and there, and whyles theyr Aduersaries haue stayed to gather that spoyle, they haue escaped. Others haue of purpose suffered theyr Ennimies to take the spoyle of theyr Carriages

Also Frote King of Denmarke in England.

and Baggages, and béyng so laden and disordered with their Spoiles, haue sette vpon them and defeated them.

Some béyng pursued by an Ennimie of force, and fyndyng themselues no waye able to deale wyth hym in Battayle, nor séeing anye other meane to saue their people, haue contrarye to all Warlike Disci-pline, caused their Souldioures to disperse themselues se-uerall wayes wythoute order, without Ensigne display-

Hannibal of Car-thage enuironed by Fabius Maxi-mus in the Mou-taines of Italy.

ed, or Drumme sounded, and euerye manne to make the beste shifte he coulde, appointing them some other place, whither suche as coulde escape, should make their repaire: and by this disorder, haue saued the greater parte of theyr people, whyche otherwise had béene assured to haue peri-shed. But this is a Pollicie neuer to be put in execution,

The Spaniardes by the Frenche pursued vppon their retire from the siege of Mar-silia in Prouence.

but vpon greate extremitie: For more honoure is it for a Generall, in common opinion, by Battel maintaining Mi-litaire Orders, to be vanquished, than by disorderly flying, in this sort to saue himself, & some parte of his people. And yet haue the moste famous Generalles vpon extremitie put it in vse, & thereby made hed againe vpon the Enimy, & re-
                                                                    couered

couered their honor, which otherwise had vtterly bin lost.

Some being inuaded by an Enimy strong in Horse, haue onely fronted him in the fielde, determining by no meanes to giue him Battell, but impaling his own Fanterie with Carriages, both Martching and Encamping hathe maintayned hymselfe in suche strength, that albeit his Armie were farre lesse, yet was it not possible for his Aduersarie with Horsemen to enter vpon him, and thereby with tyme onely hath so impouerished hys Enimie, that finding Forrage also to faile him for suche a multitude of Horse, hath bin driuen without stroke striking to retire. *The Duke of Alba against the Prince of Orange*

Some being by a Forraine Enimie inuaded, haue thoughte it the beste meanes to leuie an Armie, and likewise to inuade the Country of that Enimie : And some hauing their Countreis by Seas distoyned, after that he hadde by shipping transported his Armie, by Necessitie to make his Souldiours valiant, hathe burnte his owne Shippes, shewing his Souldiors, that nowe there was no remedy, but eyther by Victorie to commaund all, or to expecte present death, or that muche worse is, perpetuall Slauerie : And by this Necessitie his Souldioures gathering Vertue and Courage, haue obtayned their desire. *Scipio agaynst Hannibal.* *Agathocles againste the Carthagians.*

Some being inuaded by a puissaunt Enimie in the daye of Battell, haue deferred the fighte, till a good parte of the day was spent, knowing, that if their Enimie did preuaile, yet the night comming on them, they shoulde not so well be able to pursue the Victorie, but that they being in theyr own Country, and acquainted how al Straites & Passages, & places of strength lay for the, being protected by the darke night, might the better escape & make hed again vpon their Enimies. And contrariwise, if the Inuaders shoulde be broken, the night comming on them, and being ignorant of the coutry, they should haue no place of Refuge, but dispersing themselues as Fortune and Chaunce shoulde leade them, soulde not but fall into the handes of theyr Enimies, who *Iugurtha in Afrike agaynste the Romanes.*

who pꝛefently knewe al Straites and Paſſages, where to lye in readineſſe to receiue them. A pollicie not vnmæte to beremembꝛed of all ſuche as in their owne Countries are inuaded.

Some expecting the inuaſion of ſome puiſſaunte Enimie haue not leuied anye Armie of foꝛce to giue them Battell, but onely certaine ſelecte Bandes of light Hoꝛſe and Fote-men lightly armed, & cauſing all the people of the Frontiers to withdꝛawe themſelues, their Cattell, Coꝛne, and Sub-ſtaunce, into the ſtrong and foꝛtified places of the Country, haue with thoſe ſelecte Bandes faced the Ennimie on the Frontiers, by kæping of Straites and Paſſages, making ſodain attempts in the night, and ſuch other times as by eſ-piall they found the Enimie careleſſe :: And ſo with a few people, by Time, Famine, and Expences, haue wearied the Enimies, & cauſed thē retyꝛe, that happily in Battel might haue gotten the Uictoꝛie, and ſo commanded the whole.

Scanderberg a-gainſte the greate Turke.

Some being inuaded by Sea, haue immediatelye bæfoꝛe the appꝛoche of the Enimie, cauſed their Buoyes and other Sea-markes to be changed and remoued, whereby the Eni-mies miſtaking the Chanelles, haue fallen wyth the grea-ter parte of their Nauie vpon the Shelues and Sandes: And being in that ſoꝛte encombꝛed, haue bene aſſayled by thoſe their Defendaunt Ennimies, taken, ranſacked, and ſpoy-led.

The Flushin-gers againſt the Duke of Medina his Nauie.

Some inuading the Enimies Countrey, and ſpoyling all the Pꝛouince where they came, haue onelye ſpared the houſes and poſſeſſions of ſome one oꝛ other perſon among their Aduerſaries, whome they did knowe to be of grea-teſt Wiſedome and Ualure, of purpoſe to diſcredite them, and make them ſuſpected, whereby their Counſell ſhoulde not carrie Authoꝛitie, oꝛ be fallowed.

Hannibal againſt Fabius Maximus.

Some haue wꝛitten Letters to ſome of the pꝛincipall Counſelloꝛs of their Aduerſaries, as it were touching ſome pꝛactiſe of Treaſon betwæn them, and by coꝛrupted eſpiall

Practiſed by Metellus in Af-frike againſte Iugurth.

founde

founde the meanes that those Letters haue bene intercep-
ted,and brought to the General on the other side, who for
Iealousie theron conceyued, ha h not only reiected,but also
murdered those his most assured, Wise,and faithful Coun-
sellours.

Some to bring their Enimies (that were strongly encā-
med)into the playn fielde where they might fight with thē,
haue of purpose suffred some one to escape,who as a Fugi-
tiue flying to the Enimies, hath declared that there was a
Mutinie in their Campe, and immediately of purpose the
Bandes haue diuided themselues, and with Ensignes Dif-
played,martched contrariwayes, wherevpon the enimies
to vse the aduantage of this Occasiō haue left their strēgth
to pursue them: And by that Pollicie turning vppon them
haue defeated them.

Some sending Ambassadours to their Enimies,haue put
certaine of their wisest and most experte Captaines in the
habite of seruauntes and Lackeis, who comming into the
Camp of their Enimies vnder colour to folow some Horse
of theirs that of purpose they let go,haue scene,perused, and
noted many particularities,wherby they haue afterwards
assayled and defeated their enimies Armie.

Scipio to King Siphax in Aphricke.

Some haue banished some one of their most assured and
trustie seruaunts,who confedering himselfe with the Enimie, and seeming to bewray some Secrets, hath from tyme
to tyme aduertised his maister of the whole estate of his aduersaries.

Some haue corrupted the Enimies Espial, and by that
meanes abusing them, haue trayned their aduersaries into
great inconuenience: A Practise aboue all other to worke
great effectes,if it be discreetely handled.

A General may sometimes inuent and spreade Rumors
of ayde and assistaunce from Forraine Princes,or such like,
to Annimate his owne people,& terrify his aduersarie.But
such Pollicie must be vsed more rarely and with great Difcretion.   P.   The

The Actions Militare being such as require present Resolutions, and leaue no time for Consultation, a General ought always to be so prepared with prudent preconsideration, that no accident maye happen for the which he had no forethought his Remedie.

He ought by all meanes to purchace good Espial, and not to spare any charges to be wel informed from time to time of the estate of his Aduersarie, his preparation, order, furniture, and determinations, accordingly to dispose of hys owne Armie. And hereby shal a wise General, vsing Oportunitie and occasions offered, oftentimes wyth smal Troupes, do wonderfull great and famous Seruices.

I might *here adioyne another large booke of* Approching, *Besieging and winning of* Townes *and* Castels, *by* Scale, Myne, Batterie, *and* Famine: *Also the Art to* Defend, *& Garde* Forts, *& Cities, by outward & inward* Fortifications, *with sundry other* Militare Stratagemes, *and* Pollicies, *put in execution by prudet, valiaunt* Captaines, *wherby they haue attained miraculous* Victories, *and contrarie to al expectation haue escaped imminente* Perils. *For such* Precedentes *ought a wise* General *to haue readily in his memorie vpon any oportunitie offered, to be ready to put the like in execution, and to be so prepared, that no such* Accident *or mischief can happen, for the which he should not be prouided of bis* Remedie.

But *of this and many other, necessarie for the honorable charge of a* General, *I shàl haue occasion to intreate in other my* Militare *workes of* Fortificatiō *and* Pirotectny. *&c, leauing farther at this time to wade therein: Only I haue annexed two* Plats, *the one of a* Campe *to lodge* 30000 *Footemen and* 6000 *horsemen strongly and commodiously: the other is an order of* Embattelling *the same Armie in playne grounde, where the Scituation yeeldeth no aduauntage. And so I meane to finishe this Treatise.*

VIS CONSILII EXPERS, MOLE RVIT SVA.

¶ The declaration of
the Campe. Chap. 16.

Or *strong and commodious encamping of an* Armie, *the Lord* High Marſhal *is firſte to finde ſuch a place to encampe vpon, as may be conueniently woodded & watred, not ſubiect to any Hil within* Cul uering *ſhot, and to apply the forme of his Campe to the nature of the* Scituation. *But this plat I haue preſcribed where all thoſe natural helpes fayle : And that the* Generall *is to truſte onlye to his owne order , and Artificial ſtrength.*

When *any* Armie *is therefore in ſuch place to be* Encamped, *ye ſhal firſt in the moſt commodious place, about the middeſt of the grounde where yee meane to encampe, ſet vp the Generals* Stan derde, *and aboute the ſame ſtake out a ſquare plat of ground* 40 *pace ſquare for the Generals* Pauilion. *Directly from this towards the* North *runneth one mayne ſtreete* 40 *pace broade, that diui deth the* Horſe Campe *from the* Foote Campe: *And on eyther ſide of the Generals tente runneth two other croſſe wayes thirtie pace in breadth, which diuide the* Armed *from the* Vnarmed, *as hereafter ſhal appeare.*

Theſe *two wayes imbrace two long* Squares *of grounde for tie pace broade, and* 550 *pace long a peece* Theſe maye b. *eyther of them diuided into fiue lodgings of a hundred pace in length, and fortie in breadth , leauing betweene then certayne paſſages of tenne pace in breadth, that* Souldiours *vpon euerye ſuddaine maye the more readilye repayre to the place of aſſemblye.*

One

One of these lodgings next the Generals *tente may serue for the* Highmarshal *& his retinue. And the other on the other side far* the Treasurer, *the rest may be* assigned at the Marshals discrea-tion to the other Officers *of the fielde , and for* Ambassadours, and such noblemenne and Gentlemen *as follow the wars on their owne charge, and such like.*

In the Northest *quarter of the Campe are the* Horsemen lodged: *In the* Northwest *the* Footemen. *Either of these* Campes *are diuided into three partes by streates running* Easte and West. *These streetes are* 20 *pace in breadth, and* 580 *pace long. In euery of these three spaces of the* Footecampe *there are* lodged a Regiment of 1 0 0 0 0 men: *and in the* Horsecampe, *the middlemost of the shal serue for* 1500 *men at* Armes. *The Nor-then space may serue for the* 2500 Light Horsemen : *and the o-ther for the* 2000 Demilaunces.

On the other side of this mayne streete are the lodgings assig-ned for the leaders or Gouernours *of euerye regimente & their* Officers: *Euery space being* 30 *pace broade, and* 170 *long. A is for the* Captaine of the Demilaunces, B *for the* Captaine of the men at Armes. *And* C *for the* Captaine of the Light Horse-men.

Likewise D E F *for the leaders of the three principal regiments of* Footemen, *the which ye may distinguish with the vsual names,* Vawarde, Battayle, and Reregarde , *calling the* Vawarde *that which lyeth next the* Generals tente *, and aunswereth to the De-milaunces :* The Battel *that whiche aunswereth to the* men at Armes : *And the* Rerewarde *the other againste the lighte horse-men.*

Euery of these principal Regimentes *ye maye againe diuide into fiue smaller* Regimentes *by streetes of tenne pace broade, running* North *and* South *, so haue yee* fifteene *lesse* Regi-mentes *in the* Foote Campe . *And fiue a peece in euerye of the* Horse Campes : *And euerye of these* Regimentes *are* 100 *pace broade. and* 1 7 0 *pace in length . And shall* conteine conteyne euerie of them of footemen 2000, of men at armes 300, of Dimilances 400, of light Horsemen 500, with their Coronels, and their officers. &c.

These Coronels and Captaynes of men at Armes, may bee lodged at the head of their Regimentes, as you maye beholde in the Camp. Those marked with G. are for the Coronell of Footemen, H for the Captayne of light horsemen, I. for the Captaynes of men at Armes, and K. for the Captaynes of the Demilances. So remayne there Regimentes, of 100 pase broade, and 150 pase long for lodging of the Souldioures, whiche may, by small streetes of fiue pase broade, be diuided into as many spaces, as there are seuerall bands in euerie Regiment, and then the Harbinger of euery band must set downe the Officers and Souldyoures of their bands.

These last diuisions of bands I haue omitted, bycause in so small a plat it woulde breede but confusion, and the thing being of it selfe most plaine, it should be but tedious to rest longer there-vpon.

This only I would wish the Camp Mayster to obserue, that his Shot be lodged towardes the outside of the Camp, that they may be alwayes readie at the ring of the Campe vpon any Alarme. The whiche he maye do by diuiding the vtmost seauen regimentes into halfe, as you see by the pricked lines, leauing the seauen spaces marked with L. for the 7000 Shot, and the other noted with M. for 7000 Pikes, all the other Regiments marked with N. shall be the Lodgings of the 16000 short weapons.

Thus in the North moytie of your Campe, are all youre Armed both horsemen and footemen lodged.

Now the other moytie must serue for the lodging of the vnarmed, as Pioners, Carters, Carpenters, Smithes, Butchers, Victualers, and all other sortes of Mechanicall Artificers, togither with a large place of Assembly for the Souldioures to retire vnto, to put themselues in order vpon any Alarme, and also to exercise themselues in sundrie sortes of Actiuitie.

You shall therefore from the Southside of the Generals Pauilion 600 pase South vard, extend out your first maine streete of 40 pase broade, and crosse hym agayne with another streete, running East

and

and Weaſt, 360 *paſe diſtante from the Southſide of the Generalls* Pauilion. *This ſtreete neede bee but thirtie paſe in breadth.* A-*gayne, extende out the ſeconde narrowe ſtreetes, that runne para-lell to the firſte mayne ſtreete, till you come to this croſſe ſtreete laſt made, ſo haue you* O *youre place of Aſſemblie three hundred and thirtie paſe broade, and fiue hundred and fortie paſe long.* P *ſhall be appoynted for the* Munition, *and Officers attendante on the* Artillerie. Q *the Market place. Rounde aboute this Market place may be lodged the* Butchers, Bakers, Cookes, *and* Victuallers *of all ſortes.*

About *the* Munition *quarter, beſides the Officers and Gun-ners, may the* Smithes, Carpenters, Wheelewrites, *and* Labourers *attendante on the* Ordinance *be placed.*

Aboute *the place of Aſſemblie, may be the* Tentes *of all ſuch as furniſhe the* Campe *with things needefull for the* Souldioures, *as* Armourers, Taylers, Shoomakers, *and all ſuche like* Artifi-cers.

Yet *remayne there two long Squares of earth, eyther of them fiue hundred and fortie paſe long, and one hundred and nintie paſe broade : heere you maye ſettle the* Carters *and* Waggoners, *wyth their* Horſe *and* Oxen, *for the* Carriadges *themſelues muſt al-wayes* Impale *that parte of the* Campe *that is not otherwiſe by Nature or Arte* Fortifyed.

In *theſe two* Quarters *alſo maye bee lodged the* Pioners, *and all other ſortes of* Labourers, *that aptlie can not, or oughte not bee placed in or aboute the former* Courtes *or quarters of Aſſemblie.*

Laſt *of all, you ſhall deſcribe threeſcore paſe diſtante from all thoſe* Regimentes, *and their* Quarters *alreadie ſet downe, the* Ring *of the* Campe, *cauſing ſome prettie* Trenche *and* Vau-mure *to bee throwen vp, placing youre* Ordinance *vpon the ſame, as in the Figure is deſcribed, and betweene the* Ordinance *youre* Carriadges : *and this maye ſuffice, if the* Enimie *be not verie puiſſante, or neere at hande : but if you ſuſpect the arriuall of the E-*
nimie,

nimie, or that you know him stronger in the Fielde than your selfe, and woulde therefore Encampe surelie till farther ayde come vnto you, then shall you without this Ring, an hundred pase distant, cause youre Pioners and Souldioures (for vpon such occasion, hee is not woorthie to beare the name of a Souldyoure, that will not sette his hande to the spade) you shall cause them I say throw vppe another Rampire, with certaine Bulwarkes at euerie corner, and likewise in the middle of the Curtayne, that Musket Shotte maye play betweene them, or if time woulde permitte, it were conueniente euerie twelue score to haue of these Circulare Platteformes, with a Vamure, to defende the small Shotte, for in so shorte time it is impossible to make anie sufficiente Rampyre to abide a Batterie, neyther can a Campe bee furnished of Victuals to abide anie long tyme, and that is the cause why I haue described these plaine Circulare formes, which in Fortification of a Towne or Forte were meere ridiculous, and in a Campe to make them more exquisite, were no lesse foolish Curious.

The old English Encamping, noted by Guiciardine in his Italian Historie.

Howe this Campe shoulde bee Watched and Warded, I haue declared in the Office of the Scoutemayster, but what kindes of Engins may bee prepared for defence, I reserue for my Treatise of Fortification and Pyrotechny, admonishing in the meane time all suche Noble and free mindes, as take delighte in the Sciences Liberall, and couet knowledge in this Arte of greate Artillerie, or Fortification of Townes, Fortes, or Campes, agaynste the furie of this newe Engine. &c. to acquaynte themselues with so muche of the Science of Numbers, both Vulgare and Cossicall, as I haue in this Treatise taughte, and also with so muche of the Science of Geometrie, as concerneth the measuring of Lengthes, Heyghthes, and Distances, the making of Mappes, and Plattes in true measure and Proportion, and the Supputation of the contentes Superficiall, as you maye reade, at large sette downe in my other Treatise Geome-

Geometricall *named* Pantometria, *so shall they be prepared for my other workes, and for atteyning suche perfection in the Arte of* Souldiorie, *for all kindes of seruices* Offensiue or Defensiue, *by Lande or Sea in manner howsoeuer. As without these knowledges, can not be so mutch as* Aymed *at, and much lesse effectuallie atchieued.*

(∵)

LABORE ET VIGILANTIA.

¶A Declaration of the Battaile in Portraiture.

Hese Souldiers *thus orderly lodged in their seuerall* Regiments *euery one distant from other, may most easely and readily after the vsuall maner be ranged into three seueral battailes, armed with* Pikes, *and flanked with* Shot. *But bicause I haue alreadie in my* Arithmeticall *questions, vpõ the* Serieant Maiors *office declared how these kindes of embattailing, and also the* Mayne square *armed rounde with* Pikes *may be readily framed, I haue thought good heere to set downe a* forme of Battaile *more seruiceable and forcible than those cõmon* sortes.

And *although these* 30000 Footemen, *&* 6000 Horsemen, *may by the ingenious* Serieant generall *according to the nature of the* Place *be sorted and deuided into an infinite number of other seruiceable formes of* Battaile: *Yet I thought good to set downe one of that sorte, where no aduauntage is gained by the nature of the place, but that the* Generall *is onely to trust to the strength of his good order.*

And *albeit I would wish such perfection in our* Soldiorie, *as was in the* Romane, *that they might be able to fight, and retire in order, & so make many sundry* Heades *vpon the* Enimie, *if* Fortune *did abandon thẽ in the first or secõd encounter : yet cõsidering how our* Soldiorie *in these dayes are trained, I thinke it vtterly vaine to practize the* Romane *order, albeit of all other it were with perfect* Soldiors *the most* inuincible.

But *to vse still our common brute mayne* Battaile, *or three* Battailes *in one* Fronte, *committing the whole fielde to one brunte of* seruice, *as now a dayes is vsed, I hold it* barbarous, *and haue therfore in this forme of* Battaile, *that I will now set downe, sought a meane course not so exquisite, but that the* Soldiers *of our time might be able to learne, and put in execution.*

Z.   I

I *haue firſt therefore deuided the* Armie *into two* fronts *or fa-*
ces: The firſt as ye may beholde I haue ſeparated into 8 Battalions,
euery of them hauing 30 *in a ranke, and* 33 *ranckes. They are ar-*
med in the fronte with 7 *rankes of* Pikes, *all the reſt ſhort weapon,*
as Swordes *and* Targets, Halbetdes, Billes, *or ſuch like. Eue-*
ry Battalion *cõteineth* 1000 *men lacking* 10, *& are placed three*
or foure paces one from another.

The ſecond front *is deuided into* 5 *greater* Battalions, *euery*
one of them being of 2000 *men,* 40 *in a Ranke, and* 50 *Rankes, e-*
uery Battalion *armed in the* Front *with* 6 *rankes of* Pikes. *Theſe*
Battalions *are one from an other at leaſt* 25 *paſes, and the one*
Front *of Battailes from the other at leaſt* 60 *paces. In or nigh the*
middle Battalion of this ſecond Front ſhalbe the Generall *himſelfe*
when he ſeeth time.

Theſe Battalions *are impaled on either ſide with an hundred*
Ranke *of* Pikes, 7 *in a ranke, and on the* Baske *with ſixe Ranke*
of Pikes: *Without theſe haue I placed my ſhot marked with this*
ſigne ☉ *in* 24 Troupes, *euery Troupe conteining an* 100. There
is alſo in the Forelorne hope *before the face of the Battayle, like-*
wiſe 18 Troupes *of ſhot of an* 100 *a peece, their order yee maye*
note by this figure ☉: *But after they come to face the* Enemie,
they muſt Disband *and maineteine skirmiſh, as heeretofore more*
perticularly hath bene declared.

Laſt *of all are the* Winges *of* Horſemen *on either ſide, deui-*
ded into 3 Troupes. *The two firſt are the men at* Armes 30 *in a*
Ranke *and* 25 *Rankes. The two ſecond are* Demilaunces 30 *in a*
Ranke, *and* 33 *Rankes. The laſt are the* Light Horſemen 50
in a Ranke, and 25 *Rankes.*

Thus *haue ye in the firſt* Front *of* Pikes, 1680. *In the ſecond*
Front 1200. *In the* Empalement 3800. *Theſe in all amount to*
6680. *So is there lefte* 320 Pikes *to be employed in looſe ſleeues to*
accompany ſuch Shot, *and ſhort* Weapon, *as ſhal remaine for the*
garde of the Ordinaunce.

Likewiſe *in the firſt* Frunt *there are of ſhorte Weapons* 6240
in the ſecond Front 8800. *So doe remaine* 960 *ſhort Weapons to be*
imployed

imployed together with the remnaunt of the Pikes *for garde of the* Artillerie *or* Cariadges, *or els to mingle with the* Shot *in the* Forelorne hope, *the which when they shall grow pele meale with the* Enemie, *will be able to doe great seruice.*

Also after the Battailes *approch, they may retire with the* Forlorne *hope to assist their* Horsemen.

The Shot *ye may behold sorted in* Troupes 1800 *in the* Front, *& in either* Wing 2400, *so doe there remaine* 400 Shot *more to ioyne with the* Pikes *and* Short weapons *extraordinarie in anye of the foresaid seruices.*

Thus *after the great* Ordinaunce *on either side haue discharged, the* Forelorne hope *is continuallye to be supplyed with newe* Troupes *of* Shot *from the* Flankes *&* Winges, *& these* Troupes *of the* Forelorne hope *that haue dischardged shoulde retire betweene the* Battaile *& the* Troupes *of* Horse *to the* Backe *of the* Wings, *so mainetaining the* Flankes *alwaies furnished. And thus may they (being welled) mainetaine* Skirmish *continually with fresh men, and the* Battaile *always impaled.*

But *after the* Battailes *begin to approch, the* Forelorne hope *must withdraw themselues: Then is your first* Battaile *strongly fronted & impaled with* Pikes *to abide any chardge of* Horsemen, *& after their* Pikes *be broke, are together with the rest of the short weapon to deale with the* Enemie, *and during the continuance of the* Fight, *betweene these* Battalions *the* Shot *may continuallye dischardge in the face of the* Enemie.

Likewise *ther may be made certain smal* Carriadges, *some lade with* Muskets, *some with* Calabashes, *others with murderig* Fire balles: *& these* Carriages *may during the* Battaile *cotinually spoile the* Enemies Front, *being safely garded betweene the* Battallions.

The *fashion of these* Carriages, *& many other seruiceable* Engins, *not yet practized, I reserue to my treatize of* Pirotechnye *and* Fortification.

But if Fortune *should abadon them in the first encounter, & that they be broke by the* Enemies, *yet haue they those ample spaces betweene the* Battallions *of the secod* Front *to retire vnto, ther to make* Head, *and giue the* Enemie Battaile *againe.*

And these *Spaces or* Lanes *between the* Battalios *serue not only to receiue the* Skirmishers *or other that shall retire, but also for the* Messengers *which among the* Romanes *were called* Mandatores, *to passe too and fro, and to signifie to all partes from time to time the* Generalls *pleasure.*

Of the Horsemen *the men at* Armes *are first placed, who are first on the* Flanke *of the* Enimie *to giue the charge when time is. The* Demilaunces *are to followe them if they haue* victorie, *or to assist them if they be repulsed or charged by the* Enemie: *And the* Bandes *of* Light *horsmen to giue ayde to them both, and also to follow the chase when the* Footemen *are broken.*

What scope of ground this whole Battaile, *& particularly, euery of his* Battallions, Troupes, Empalements, &c. *requireth, the* Scale *discouereth: And superfluous were it to vse moe wordes in this matter.*

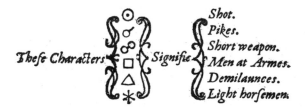

These Characters } *Signifie* { Shot.
Pikes.
Short weapon.
Men at Armes.
Demilaunces.
Light horsemen.

FABER EST QVISQVÆ FOR-
TVNÆ SVÆ.

¶Certeine *Questions* in the Arte of *Artillerie*, by *Mathematical Science* ioyned vvith Experience, tobe deba-ted *and discussed.* Chap.18.

He *diuersitie of the force &* violence *of great Ar-tillerie* , *& of the farre or nigh shooting & variable* randge *of their* Bullets, *doth chiefely arise & grow of these* 4 *principall causes:* Powder, Peece, Bullet, *&* Randõ. *In* Powder *is cõsidered Quantitie & Qualitie. In the* Peece *the length & proportiõ of the* Cylinder. *In the* Bullet *his waight & Quantitie. In* Randon *the degrees of* Altitude *frõ the* Horizon *or plain wher the* Peece *must play. These may be called the Prime, substantiall or effectuall causes.*

There *are also other causes and circumstaunces which may like-wise worke some alteration: as the* Raritie *or Densitie of the ayre.* The Winde. *The diuers* wadding *and* ramming *in chardging.* The *inequalitie of the ground or* Plat-forme, *and wheeles of the* Carriadge *reculing. The regular or irregular* Boring. *The distẽ-pering of the* Peece *hotte or colde, and well or ill fitting the* Bullet. *These may be termed secondarie or* accidentall *causes of altera-*tion, *which by* Practize *and vse will best be learned, and their er-*rours *by discretion reformed, albeit for some of them certain* Rules *may also be prescribed.*

But *these* Questions *ensuing, are onely of such* Alterations *as grow by those first foure* principal *or substantiall causes, supposing all these other* accidentall *by good discretion well ordered and vni-formely guyded. And first of* Powder.

Of Povvder.

VVHether *there be not for any* Peece *proponed, such a cer-taine* Quantitie *of* Powder *to be found, as dnely to the*

chardge

charge of the same Peece agreeth, and that in such sort that charging the Peece with more or lesse than that Quantitie, it shall hinder the farre ranging of the Bullet.

2 Whether one & the selfe same Peece twice charged with one & the selfe same Quãtitie of Powder & Bullet, discharged also at the same Randon, shal make the same Randges, hauing all one manner of Chardging, Wadding & Ramming.

3 If a Peece be discharged with the waight of his Bullet in Serpentine Powder, & afterwards againe discharged with the half waight of his Bullet in such Corne powder as shall cause the Peece to cast the same ground, I demaund if the same Peece bee again charged with halfe the quantitie of either sort, whether these second Randges shall also be equall? the forme of charging being vniforme, and temper of the Peece all alyke.

4 If two Peeces of the same Length & Bullet be charged with one kinde of Pouder, but seuerull Waights, I demaund whether the Randges shalbe proportionall to the said waights, or to ½ ⅔ or ⅞ Rootes of the said waights, or whether the proportiõ of those Rã ges be not to be foũd without any farder respect either to the Lẽgth of the Peece or Ponderositie of the Bullet, considering by Hipothesis al those are equall.

5 Whether the Proportion found in one kinde of Pouder, hold not in al other kindes, of what mixture soeuer it be, the Peeces and Bullets being as is before supposed equall.

6 One Peece being charged first with one quarter of the waight of the Bullet, after with one halfe finally with the whole Waight & the Ranges of the Bullet at Point Blanke noted, I demaũd Whether the same Ranges be not Proportional, al circumstaunces of charging &c. being vniforme.

7 Whether the Proportion of such Ranges be not a meane proportional resulting of the commixtion of the Equalitie of the Peeces Lengths and Bullets, and of the Inequalitie of the Powders Quantitie, the Qualitie being supposed lyke.

Of the length of the Peece and Pouder.

VVHether two Peeces being in al respects equal, sauing on-

ly

ly in Length, *being charged with one* Bullet, *and one* Quantitie *of* Powder *shall not make seuerall* Grazes.

2 Whether *the longer* Canon *shal make the greater* Range, *what soeuer* Quātitie *or kinde of* Powder *they be discharged withall, the* Quantitie *of* Powder *being equall.*

3 Whether *there be not a certen cōuenient* Length *of the* Peece *in respect of his* Bore *or* Bullet, *to make the vtmost* Randge, *in such sort that the making of the* Canon *longer shall rather hinder than furder.*

3 Whether *this* Length *and* Proportion *being found in one* Peece *hold in all other (the proportion I meane) for the length must of necessitie alter.*

4 The Proportion *being by* Experience *found with* Serpētine Pouder *acording to the ordinary charge, whether giuing like quātitie of* Corne Pouder, *the same* Proportiō *of perfectiō shal hold, or a new be to be sought in respect of the alteration of the* Pouder.

6 If *two* Peeces *being in al respects equal saue onely in* Length, *being discharged with one* Bullet *&* Quantitie *of one sort of* Pouder *make seuerall* Randges *at* Point blanke *discharged : I demaund whether the same proportion of* Ranges *shall still continue with what soeuer* Quantitie *or kinde of* Pouder *the same* Peeces *be charged? the* Quantitie *being alway equall & all other circūstaunces of charging & discharging in either of them lyke.*

If *two* Peeces *in al respects like saue only in* Length *be charged with one* Bullet, *and the waight of the same* Bullet *in ordinarie* Serpentine Pouder, *I demaūd whether their* Ranges *shal beare the proportiō of the lēgth of their* Canōs, *or of the* Vacant hollow Canōs *frō the* Charge *to the* Mouth. *Or if it bere not the same proportiō, whether they cary not the proportion, of the* ⅟₄ *or* ℈ ⅞ *Rootes considering al other circumstaunces being* Equall *saue only the* Longitude *of the* Canons, *it is apparaunt that from their proportion as the original cause, the* Proportion *of the* Ranges *must in this case be deriued.*

8 If *ther be* 3 Peeces *in al respects equal saue only in lēgth of their* Canōns *or* Cilinders *& yet those* 3 Lōgitudes *proportional, I demaund whe-*

whether the ranges of their Bullets shall not be proportionall, all o-
ther circumstaunces saue onely this of Lengthes, being one, equall
and like.

9 If ther be 3 Peeces, as afore, hauing the Lōgitude of their hollow or vacāt Cilinders proportionall, whether thē all the rest being
equall and vniforme, the Ranges shall not be proportionall.

10 Or if in one of these cases the proportion of the Ranges be not
a meane proportionall resulting of the commixtion of the Equalitie
of the Bullets weights, the Equalitie of the Pouder, and the Inequalitie of the longitude of the Cylinders either whole or vacāt.

Of the Povvder and length of the
Peece considered with the Bullet.

IF a Peece be twice discharged with one quantitie of the same
Powder, but the Bullets in waight different, I demaund whether the lighter shal alway out-flye the heauier, or that some conuenient waight may be found.

2 Whether this conuenient waight of the Bullet alter not according to the Quantitie or validitie of the Powder.

3 Whether to finde the said conuenient Ponderositie of the
Bullet it be sufficiēt to consider the Powder, or that the Lōgitude
of the Peece also cause therein a diuersitie.

4 If a Peece be twice charged, first with an Iron, then with a
Ledde shot, the quantities of Powder at both times equall: whether the difference of the ranges be not deriued onely from the proportion of the waights of these bullets, all other circumstaunces by
Hinpothesis differing not. And what relation to the Ponderositie of the Bullets these Ranges haue.

5 Two Peeces being in all respects equall and charged with
one kinde of Powder, but different Bullets, the one Iron, the other
Lead, and either hauing the waight of his Bullet, I demaund whether the Ranges be equall.

6 If one Peece be charged three seuerall times, first with a
Stone

stone Bullet, *then with* Iron, *finally with* Lead, *& the Iron of such*
temper that it be an exact meane proportional in wayght betweene
the other two, being al discharged with one quantitie of Pouder, *I*
demaund whether the Randges *shal be in continual proportion.*

7 *If a* Peece *be twice charged, first with* Iron, *then with* Lead,
hauing one quantitie of Pouder, *and the* Ranges *noted: I demand*
whether being charged with any other quätity of Pouder, *the* Räges *of the same Bullets shal not alway retain the same proportiö.*

8 *The* Proportion *found by* experience *in one* Peece *of the*
different Randges *that Iron and Lead Bullets make, whether the*
same proportion hold in any other Peece *longer or shorter, shooting*
the same Bullets, *whatsoeuer hir length bee.*

9 *If in a* Faulcon *for example, by experience I finde two suche*
quantities of Pouder, *as discharging the* Falcö *with the first quä*
titie of Pouder *with an Iron shot : and again discharging hir with*
the second quätitie & a Lead shot, they range both duely one groüd:
I demaüd whether in a Saker *of the same length with the* Falcö,
charging hir first with an Iron Bullet, thë with a Lead Bullet, vsing
the same quantities of Pouder, whether their Randges shal be pro
portional. And whether dubling either quantitie of Pouder, it shall
alter the proportion of the Randges.

10 *If two* Peeces *of one length be of such differët* Quantitie *of*
Bullet *that the one being discharged with a Lead Bullet, the other*
with an Iron Bullet, either hauing of Pouder the waight of their
Bullet, and do so make equal Ranges: I demaunde whether either of
them discharged with halfe the waight of their Bullets in Pouder
shal Range alike also.

11 *If two* Peeces *be of one length, but of seueral quätity of Bul*
let, and yet of one kind of Metal *or substance, and discharged with*
the waight of the Bullet in one kinde of Pouder, *I demaunde whe*
ther they shal not range one ground being equally mounted.

12 *If there be once found by experience in some one* Peece *such*
a perfection of a Canon, *as whether ye make him longer or shorter*
he shal shoote lesse grounds, hauing alway the waight of his Bullet
of one kind of Pouder *to his charge, I demaund whether if another*

&.

Peece

Peece *whose* Cannõ *or hollow* Cylinder *is in proportiõ like to the same though greter in quantitie, shal not be of the like perfection.*

13 If *two* Peeces *hauing their hollow* Cylinders Similes *or proportional , be discharged with the waight of their Bullets in* Pouder *at like* Randon *, I demaunde the proportion of the Ranges, the quantitie of their* Cylinders *knowen.*

14 Of any *two* Peeces *presented , to knowe which shal shoote farthest being both charged with the waighte of their* Bullet *in* Pouder, *the force of the* Pouder *being first in some one approued.*

15 Anye *two* Peeces *being proponed, how to charge them with such quantities of* Pouder *as they may both at like* Randons Rãge *like ground.*

16 Hauing *proued any* Peece *at his vtmost Randon with anye one kinde of Pouder, to know howe to diminish the proportion of the* Pouder *frõ time to time in suche proportion as the* Peece *keeping that* Randon *shal shoote any part you wil assigne of the first* Shot.

Of Randons.

SEeing it is by experience found, that euery *Peece* of *Ordinaunce* being at the *Leuel* or point *Blancke* discharged, throweth forth his *Bullet* with such *Violence* that it passeth a good distaunce directly without any sensible *Inclination* or touching of the grounde, the firste *Graze* that it maketh I terme the *Leuel Raunge* : and the same may also be called the righte line of the *Leuel Raunge*, the *Peece* being on Leuel grounde, and not mounted on a *Platforme.* In like sorte if a *Peece* mounted at any Randon be discharged, the *Bullet* first violently issueth out a good distance directly without making any sensible declination from the right line, by the *Axis* of the *Peece* determined, and that *Distaunce*, maye bee termed the right line of the *Randon Angle*, hereof ariseth a question.

1 Whether *the righte line of the vtmost* Randon *be equal to the right line of the* Leuel *Range , or whether in al* Peeces *they retaine one* Proportion.

2 Whether *the right line of the vtmost range be not lesse than*

the right line of 90 grades of Randon.

3 Whether *the right line of vtmost Range be a* Meane Proportional *betweene the right line of the Leuel, and the right line of the* Vertical Range, *viz. mounted 90 grades.*

4 Whether *the righte line of vtmoste Randon be not rather a* Meane Proportionall *betweene the righte line of the* Leuell Range *and that Grade of Randon that raungeth the grounde of the* Leuel Raunge.

5 Whether *the right lines made by any two* Peeces *at one* Rã-don *discharged, be not* Proportional *to the* Ranges *of their Bullets at the same* Randon.

6 Whether *the right lines made by any two* Peeces *at any* Rãdon, *be not* Proportional *with their vtmost* Ranges.

7 Whether *the vtmost* Randon, *I meane, to make the vtmoste* Range, *be always one, whether the ground be* Leuel *or ascending.*

8 Whether *the* Bullet *end his Range with a line not sensiblye different from a straight line, as it doth begin his circuite.*

9 Whether *al* Peeces *at one Randon discharged, as they make one* Angle *at the beginning of their course, do also make one* Angle *at the ende of their race.*

10 Whether *the* Angle *at the end of the* Circuite *made with the* Bullet *be equal with the* Angle *of* Randon.

11 Whether *the vpper part of the* Circuite *made by the* Bullet *be a portion of a* Circle *as* Tartalea *supposeth.*

12 Whether *it be not rather a* Conical Section *and different at euery seueral* Randon.

13 Whether *it be not at the vtmost* Rãdon *a* Sectiõ Parabolical *in al kind of* Peeces, *and to differ in greatnesse according to the greatnesse of the* Cone *that to euery seueral* Cylinder *or* Peece *of* Ordinaunce *is conuenient, being Proportionally charged according to the perfection heretofore mentioned.*

14 Whether *at al inferiour* Rãdons *that* Arke *by* Tartalea *Imagined Circular, be not an* Eleipsis, *& the same altering according to the capacitie of the* Cone *to the* Peece *appropriate, & also according to the difference of the* Angle *of* Randon.

15 If the quantitie of the Cone to euerye Peece proportionallie charged, be by experience founde, I demaunde whether then this Eleipsis shal not make an Angle with the Parabola Section equal to the distaunce betweene the grade of Randon proponed, and the grade of vttermost Randon.

16 Whether in al Randons aboue the vttermost, the sayde Curue Arke, be not an Hyperbole.

17 Whether the same Hyperbole do not also alter at euery seuerall Randon, aboue the sayd vtmost Randon.

18 Whether the Hyperbole that deliuereth this Curue Ark, be not such a Section as maketh with the Axis of the Cone, an angle equal to the Angle of the Randons Complement.

19 Whether in euerie of the Elepseical and Parabolical Sections there be not a continual alteration of the Angle of the Cone also in respect of the newe Angle of Randon.

20 Whether the Parabolical Section be not made at 45 Grades of Randon, rather than at the Grade of vtmost Randon, and so the Hyperbole at al Randons aboue, and the Elepseis at al inferiour Randons in manner before expressed.

THese may suffise to giue some tast how large a Sea of Inuentions ý ingenious Mathematitian hath to wade in, ý wil aspire to the perfection of the Art of handling gret Artilerie, & also how far off such Cannoniers are frō the first Elements of that Science, that being able to make some fair shotte from their ordinarie Plat formes, to their vsuall beaten Marks, do thinke theselues therfore perfit Masters. But as it is vtterly impossible for Archimedes himself (if he wer liuing) without Experience, long Practise, & sundrie trials, to demostrate ý manifold varieties of that mixt Helical Arcke or circuite of the Bullet, componed of violente, & natural motions, recepuing infinite diuersitie, according to the seueral proportiō of their Temperature: So is it far more impossible & absurde to imagine, that any ignorant of those Sciences, should euer be able to approche the Gates of that

Arte,

Art, hitherto by no Nation to any purpose handled. For to
passe ouer the apparaunt Errours of Daniel Santbech the
German in his booke *de Artificio Eiaculandi Spheras Tormen-
tarias* : the false Rules of Girolamo Ruchellye, and grosse
errors of many others, that being ignoraunt of the Mathematicals, haue take vpon them to write of this Arte: Euen
Tartalea the Italian, albeit he were an excellent Geometer,
taking vpon him to deliuer sundrie Demonstrations in this
newe Science, yet for wante of Practise , and Experience,
hath erred euen in the first Principles, and so consequentlye
in the whole substaunce of his discourse. This Tartalea a-
uerreth the Angle of 45 grades, as meane betwéen the Ho-
rizontal and Vertical mountes or Eleuations, to be the Angle of the vtmost Randons : an Errour knowen euen to the
first Practicioners. He affirmeth also the declining Arcke of
the Bullet to be a Section Circulare: an Errour likewise, but
not so easie to be discerned. And whereas great Fame hathe
bene spreade of certaine Tables by him inuented, to declare
the different Ranges of Bullets from al sorts of Peeces deliuered at al Grades of Randon (a matter in déede rare, and
of great inuention) thus much I dare truely auowe and ap-
proue, that Tartalea vppon those his fallible groundes & Erronious principles , was neuer possibly able in those maters
to deliuer anye certaintie. The fame among other was indéede by my father long practised, who ioyning continuall
experience for many yeres with Geometrical Demonstrations, sought, and at last founde, and did frame an Instru-
ment, with certaine Scales of Randons to performe all that
by Tartalea his Tables promised. As also by Reflection of
Glasses to fire Pouder, and discharge Ordinaunce manye
miles distaunt. And such was his Foelicitie and happie successe, not only in these Conclusions, but also in the Optikes
and Catoptrikes , that he was able by Perspectiue Glasses
duely scituate vpon conuenient Angles, in such sorte to discouer euery particularitie in the Countrey rounde aboute,

wherefoeuer the Sunne beames mighte pearfe: As fithence
Archimedes, (Bakon of Oxforde only excepted) I haue not
read of any in Action euer able by meanes natural to performe ý like. Which partly grew by the aide he had by one
old written booke of the fame Bakons Experiments, that by
ftraunge aduenture, or rather Deftinie, came to his hands,
though chiefelye by conioyning continual laborious Practife with his Mathematical Studies.

The which vpon this occafion I thought not amiffe to
rehearfe, as wel for the knowen Veritie of the matter (diuerfe being yet aliue that can of their own fight and knowledge beare faithful witneffe, thefe Conclufions being for
pleafure commonlye by him with his friendes practifed) as
alfo to animate fuch Mathematitians as enioye that quiet
and reff, my froward Conftellations haue hitherto denyed
me, to imploy their ftudies & trauels for Inuention of thefe
rare feruiceable Secretes. But fuch is my harde Deftinie,
that as Gods pleafure was to take my Father from me in
my yong and tender yeares, and euen at that verie tyme
when I began to grow capable of thofe Secretes, and him
felfe (hauing bene long debarred his owne inheritaunce &
natiue Soyle being reftoared) ment then immediately to returne to his wonted places of Exercife, there to haue deliuered me experimentally thofe the fruites of his long Trauels, & Practifes. So fithence his death, hauing foftered by
ftudie and conference thofe Theorical fparkes Mathematicall from infancie by him impreffed, after I grewe to fome
Maturitie of yeares, and iudgement, fitte to enter into triall and practife of thefe Conclufions, by continuall Lawe
Brables, (being torments as repugnant to my Nature as
the Infernal Furies to Celeftial Mufes) I haue for manye
yeres bene fo vexed and turmoyled, and from thofe delectable Studies violently haled, ý of all thofe rare Conclufions
and Secrets I haue fcarfely hitherto had any time of repofe
or quiet to wade effectually in any one, faue onelye that of
                                                    great

great Artilerie, wherin also there are yet many Mysteries that by farther profes, and trials Experimental, I muste resolue, before I can reduce that Art to suche perfection as can content me . But so sone as by Gods ayde I shall vntwine my self out of this miserable Labyrinth, wherein so long I haue bene snared, my first Endeauours shal be entierly to finishe the Treatise of that newe Science of maneoging this newe furious Engine & rare Inuention of great Artilerie, in such perfection as hitherto hath not bene in any language imparted with anye Nation of Europe.

VIRESCET VVLNERE VIRTVS.

IMPRINTED AT LON-
don, by Henrie Bynneman, dwel-
ling in Thames Street, neere vnto
Baynardes Castle.
Anno. 1579.